LeA

632.96
SAT

BIOLOGICAL PEST CONTROL

T.V. SATHE
and
P.M. BHOJE

2000
DAYA PUBLISHING HOUSE
DELHI-110 035

© AUTHORS, 2000

TUKARAM VITHALRAO SATHE (b. 1953-)
PRAKASH MARUTI BHOJE (b. 1965-)

ISBN 81-7035-225-8

Published by   :   **Daya Publishing House**
                              1123/74, Deva Ram Park
                              Tri Nagar, Delhi-110 035
                              Phone : 7103999
                              Fax : (011) 7198902
                              E-mail : info@dayabooks.com
                              Website : www.dayabooks.com

Laser Composed by :   **Vaishnav Graphics & Systems**
                              New Delhi - 110 055

Printed at   :   **Chawla Offset Printers**
                              Delhi-110052

PRINTED IN INDIA

PREFACE

Insect pest management is a chronic problem of agriculture and several other areas. It is estimated that more than Rs. 500 crores are lost annually due to pest ravages alone in our country. Hence, pesticides are widely used in pest management programmes. However, pesticides create many serious problems like heath hazards, air and water pollution, killing of beneficial insects, pest resistance, pest resurgence, secondary pest outbreak, etc. These facts indicate that there is an urgent need to develop newer approach to manage the insect pests. Biological pest control is one of the most suitable and widely accepted approach to chemical control. Biological control is designed with braconid parasitoids as they parasitize the pest species and cause mortalities in them. Therefore, they have great significance in pest management. The present work will add relevance by providing information on pest-parasitoid index, description, distribution and host records of braconid parasitoids for utilising them in biological pest control programmes.

I hope that the book will be helpful to students, teachers and researchers in the field of biological pest control.

P.M. Bhoje
T.V. Sathe

CONTENTS

Preface   iii

Ch.1   Introduction   1-5

Ch.2   Material and Methods   6-13

Ch.3   Taxonomy   14-94

     Family   : Braconidae
     Sub Family   : Microgastrinae
     Tribe   : Cotensinii
     Genus   : *Cotesia Cameron*
             Cotesia anari sp. nov.
             Cotesia arachi sp. nov.
             Cotesia bazari sp. nov.
             Cotesia chiloi sp. nov.
             Cotesia janati sp. nov.
             Cotesia mangiferi sp. nov.
             Cotesia parnari sp. nov.
             Cotesia sunflowari sp. nov.
             Cotesia tuski sp. nov.

     Genus   : *Dolichogenidea* Viereck
             Dolichogenidea exiguvi sp. nov.
             Dolichogenidea lycoperci sp. nov.
             Dolichogenidea mythimna sp. nov.
             Dolichogenidea sunflowari sp. nov.

     Genus   : *Glyptapenteles Ashamead*
             Glyptapenteles melentis sp. nov.

     Genus   : *Hypomicrogaster* Ashmead
             Hypomicrogaster minari sp. nov.

Ch.4   Biological Control   95-101

Ch.5   Aspects of Biological Control   102-109

Ch.6   Summary   109

Bibliography   110-117

Index   119-122

CHAPTER 1
INTRODUCTION

Taxonomy has never been an attractive profession since it is regarded as unrewarding and treated step motherly by financial agencies and students find fields like molecular biology, etc. But, today, the picture is in favour of taxonomy and taxonomists. Taxonomy plays a very important role in applied biology viz. public health, environmental problems, national defence, pest management, wild life management, etc. The taxonomist are needed for the identification of the species, to study the evolutionary history and guide the explorations for native and exotic species of bio-control agent. Hence, they are getting full honour and positions in Research Institutes, Museums, Universities, Central and State Government agencies, Zoos, Industries, etc.

In recent years, there are several reports on the existence of variants which react differently under different conditions, causing setbacks in applied research programmes. Biological control is one of the several areas of biological applied research which depends heavily on taxonomy. There are many reports which reveal that bio-control programmes have failed due to the incorrect species identity.

The parasitic hymenoptera is very important component of biological control since it act as bio-control agents. Kerrich (1960) believes that Hymenoptera may contain about 5 lakhs of parasitic wasps.

According to Gupta (1988) more than 1,00,000 species have been described from only two families viz., Ichneumonidae and Braconidae. Among the parasitic families of Hymenoptera, the braconidae alone consists more than 40,000 species (Achterberg, 1988) and only from USSR territory more than 1100 species have been reported (Tobias, 1976).

1

Though braconids are widely attempted from different parts of world, very little attention is paid on this group from oriental region. Only 1/10 of the species have been described (Bhat & Gupta 1977). Hence, our knowledge on oriental braconidae is meager. As far as Indian braconids are concerned, no comprehensive volume has ever been published except Bhat & Gupta (1977).

The workers of 18th century viz. Brulle (1846), Smith (1860), Cameron (1891, 1900, 1905-7, 1910 a,b,c, 1911, 1912, 1913) have described good number of genera and species of the oriental branconidae and also provided key to certain genera and subfamilies of braconidae. The notable workers on Indian braconids are Bingham (1901), Ayyar (1920, 1921, 1926, 1928), Wilkinson (1927, 1928 a,b, 1929, 1930, 1932 a,b, 1935), Watanabe (1934-1937), Beeson & Chatterjee (1935), Chatterjee (1941), Lal (1939, 1942), Narayanan (1936), Mathur (1942) and Bhatnagar (1948), etc. These workers have revised many subfamilies and genera of oriental region. The other workers like Rao & Kurian (1950), Gupta (1957), Narayanan & Subba Rao (1960), Rao (1953, 1961), Rao & Chalikwar (1970 a,b,c 1971), etc. have also contributed on braconids.

Wilkinson (1928 a,b) revised Indo-Australian species of braconids particularly the genus *Apanteles* by providing key to the species of genus *Apanteles*. Later, Rao (1961) provided a key for the oriental species of genus *Apanteles* (Braconidae). In 1967 Nixon contributed to the Ultor group of *Apanteles* with some new descriptions of the species and by providing key to the species of Indo-Australian region. Papp (1986, 1987) reported *glomeratus* group of *Apanteles*. Likely Chalikwar *et al.* (1982), Sathe and Inamdar (1988, 1989 a,b; 1991), Sathe *et al.* (1989, 1994), Sumodan & Narendran (1990), etc., have worked on Indian Microgastrinae.

Recently, Sathe (1992), Dawale *et al.* (1992, 1993); Narendran *et al.* (1992, 1994), Ingawale & Sathe (1993); Sathe *et al.* (1994), Narendran *et al.* (1994), Sathe & Ingawale (1995), Narendran & Rema (1996), Rema & Narendran (1996), Achterberg & Narnedran (1997), etc. have made significant contribution to Indian braconids. At present irrespective of efforts made by various workers, very less attention is being paid to the taxonomy of braconids. Keeping in view all facts mentioned above, the present-topic has been selected.

The braconids are grouped under sub family Microgastrinae of family Braconidae of order-Hymenoptera (Fig. 12, 24, 26, 27).

The members of family braconidae are mainly characterised by :

(1) Propodeum sculptured usually with more or less clear space,

(2) Groove between first and second tergite of abdomen,

(3) Hind wing has long submedial cell, several time wider than medial cell and

(4) Second recurrent vein absent on the fore wing,

Mason (1981) visualized 21 subfamilies of family braconidae and most important among them is Microgastrinae as it attacks macro & micro Lepidopterous, Coleopterous and Hemipterous pests.

The sub-family Microgastrinae is characterized by 16 jointed flagellum and the spiracle of laterotergite first.

Mason (1981) gave plesiomorphic characters for the Braconidae, only those that are seen useful in separating Microgastrinae from other braconids which include : vannal lobe of hind wing large and delimited distally by a notch, intercubitellan (2 r m) present, interradiallan (r) present and larval palpi developed as l-jointed sclerotized appendages.

As Micrograstrinae attack the Lepidopterous hosts (Fig. 37), it has tremendous economic significance. Under Microgastrinae, Foerster kept 3 genera viz., *Microgaster, Microplitis* and *Apanteles.* In addition, he also treated *Adelius* Haliday (1833), *Mirax* Haliday (1833), and *Dirrhope* Foerster (1851) under Microgastrinae. However, *Fornica* Brulle was variously treated but often added to Microgastrinae. Nixon (1965) added *Adelius, Paradelius, Dirrhope* and *Oligoneorus* under this sub-family, but, he made three tribes : *Cardiochiles* and its close relatives, *Mirax* and the traditional genera *Microgaster, Microplitis* and *Apanteles.* However, recently, Mason (1981) judged that there are no strong enough synapomorphic characters to group *Mirax, Cardiochiles* and *Microgastrini* in one sub family. Hence, he visualized three sub-families i.e. Microgastrinae, Miracinae and Cardiochilinae.

According to Mason (1981) Microgastrinae split into 4 tribes viz., Apanteleni, Microgastrini, Cotesiini and Microplitini. The tribe Apantelini represented by :

(i) Ovipositor sheath short, almost (97 per cent) longer than half the hind tibia, hairy throughout.

(ii) Hypopygium usually large and medially desclerotized, longitudinally striate, and often folded.

(iii) Tergite first usually longer than broad and often with a median broad groove on the apical half, tergite second usually wider than long and shorter than tergum third.

(iv) Propodeum with a partial to complete areolet; the areolet has the appearance of a 'U' or 'V' and sometimes the propodeum entirely carinate.

(v) Anterior margin of metanotum usually withdrawn from scutellar margin laterally, Prepectal carina never present, notauli absent or weakly indicated.

(vi) Antennal articles mostly with two ranks of placodes, at least on the central segments.

In the tribe Apantelini, Mason visualized 15 genera namely *Apanteles, Dolichogenidea, Exoryza, Micropotes, Semionis, Dasylagon, Sendaphne, Promicrogaster* and the new genera, *Pelicope, Teremys, Exulonyx, Ilidops, Pholetesor, Aplhomelon* and *Papanteles.*

The tribe Microgastrini is characterized by :

(1) Ovipositor sheath longer than half of hind tibia and always hairy throughout its length.

(2) Hypopygium usually large, tergite first usually longer than broad, tergite second variable, most often rectangular and little shorter than tergum third.

(3) Propodeum always with a strong, recurrent median carina.

(4) Metanotum always with sublateral setose lobes low and closely pressed to the hind margin of the scutellum, prepectal carina always absent.

Under microgastrinae, Mason (1981) reported 13 genera namely : *Hypomicrogaster, Prasmodon, Paroplitis, Hygroplitis,*

Choeras, Microgaster, Xanthomicrogaster, Clarkinella, Xenogaser, Iconella Sathon, Rhygoplitis & Pseudapanteles.

The tribe Cotesiini is confirmed by :

(i) Tergites extremely variable. Tergite first sometimes with a sharp median groove occupying the basal half or more.

(ii) Ovipositor sheath almost always shorter than half of hind tibia and few hairs are concentrated near the apex.

(iii) Propodeum with a median longitudinal carina, rarely with other strong carinae.

(iv) Antennal articles mostly with two ranked placodes but, rarely these all irregularly arranged. In female, with very short antennae, placodes are arranged in single rank on each article.

(v) Metanotum often lacking setae on sublateral lobes, the phragma more or less exposed, prepectal carina always absent.

Mason (1981) included 17 genera under Cotesiini tribe; namely, *Cotesia, Parapanteles, Glyptapanteles, Protapanteles, Larissimus, Protomicroplitis, Parenion, Buluka* and *Dolichogaster* and the new genera, *Distastris, Deuterixus, Exis, Nyereria, Rasivalva, Venanides, Venanus* and *Wilkinsonellus.*

Since the above three tribes are very much economically important, hence, in the present study attention was concentrated on them. In the present dessertation, nine species of *Cotesia*, four species of *Dolichogenidia* and one each from *Hypomicrogaster* and *Glyptapanteles* were described for the first time from India. A distributional record and host record of braconid parasitoids have also been studied and presented in the text.

In the past, from India, very few workers (Chalikwar *et al.* 1984, Sathe & Inamdar, 1989, 1991; Inamdar, 1990; Dawale, 1991; Ingawale, 1991; Dawale *et al.* 1993; Sathe *et al.* 1994; Rokade, 1996; etc.) have attempted the braconid genera, *Cotesia, Dolichogenidea, Hypomicrogaster* and *Glyptapanteles*. Considering importance of the species of above genera in biological pest control, the present work has been carried out. The present work, will be helpful for preparing host parasitoid index, ecological studies and biological control of insect pests.

CHAPTER 2
MATERIAL AND METHODS

Extensive survey of Braconid flies was made from the various districts of Maharashtra State (Plate I) from June 1994-June 1998 and a very large number of specimens were collected from the Agricultural crops. The insects were collected early in the morning and evening. Many times, parasitized larvae of Lepidoptera and cocoons of braconids were also collected on host plants and reared in the laboratory. The specimens were preserved by killing in cyanide killing bottle and kept in 90 per cent alcohol / 4 per cent formalin. Some of the braconids were pinned and kept in the insect box. The detailed records were made about the locality, date of collection, name of collector and possible identification. The head, antenna, propodeum, wings, legs, tergites ovipositor and ovipositor sheath were mounted on slides in D.P.X. Morpohological studies were carried out with the help of monocular microscope. Body length of specimens was calculated with the help of graduated mechanical stage. All measurements were made in millimeters with the help of ocular micrometer.

The braconid parasitoids were identified by consulting Wilkinson (1928 a,b), Rao (1961), Nixon (1965, 1967), Mason (1981) and Papp (1986, 1987). For the easy and exact understanding of the terms, the terminology adopted here is same as that of Mason (1981) in the description of the species.

Distributional Record

Distributional records were made by observing and collecting the braconids from various places of Maharashtra (Plate I) at one month interval.

Host Record

Host record of braconids were made by collecting the parasitized hosts and rearing them under laboratory condition (25 ± 1°C, 60-65 R.H., 12 hr. photoperiod) for the adult emergence and identification.

A large number of references were consulted in the course of the studies, those listed, are not cited in the text of the thesis.

The terms adopted in the thesis for head, thorax, wing venation and leg are as follows :

Photography

The whole mounts of the braconids and the various morphological parts viz. antenna, propodeum, wings, leg, tergites and ovipositor were considered for microscopic photography.

The photography was made by magnifying the whole mounts 10 times to its original. The wings have been magnified to 16 times and rest of the parts 25.2 times only. The photography of whole mounts was made with the help of Asahi Pentax Auto Bellows K Set Camera while, the rest of the parts were photographed by Leitz Orthoplan Microscope (Germany).

PLATE - I

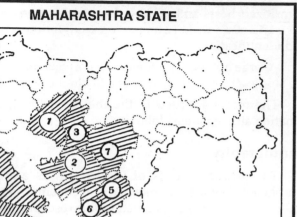

MAHARASHTRA STATE

01.	AURANGABAD	:	Bidkin.
02.	BEED	:	Chausala.
03.	JALNA	:	Shahgad.
04.	KOLHAPUR	:	Borpadle, Gaganbawada, Kalamba, Kagal, Karveer, Malkapur, Panhala, Sambhapur, Shahuwadi, Warnanagar.
05.	LATUR	:	Murud.
06.	OSMANABAD	:	Sarola.
07.	PARABHANI	:	Parbhani.
08.	PUNE	:	Chakan.
09.	SANGALI	:	Islampur, Kasegaon, Palus, Petnaka.
10.	SATARA	:	Dahiwadi, Karad, Mayani, Pal, Phaltan, Surul, Waduj.

PLATE - II

HEAD OF BRACONID : FRONT & DORSAL VIEW

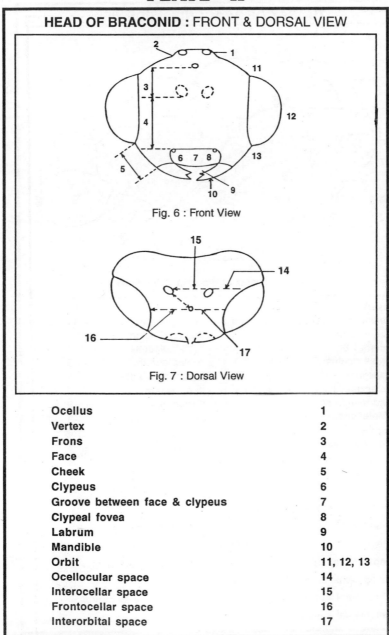

Fig. 6 : Front View

Fig. 7 : Dorsal View

Ocellus	1
Vertex	2
Frons	3
Face	4
Cheek	5
Clypeus	6
Groove between face & clypeus	7
Clypeal fovea	8
Labrum	9
Mandible	10
Orbit	11, 12, 13
Ocellocular space	14
Interocellar space	15
Frontocellar space	16
Interorbital space	17

PLATE - III

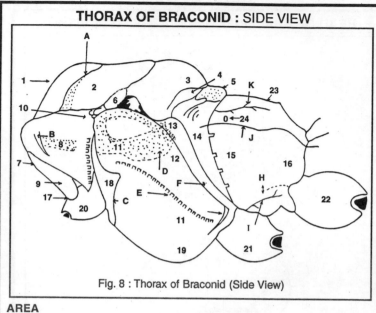

Fig. 8 : Thorax of Braconid (Side View)

AREA

Median lobe of Mesonotum	1 and 2	Mesopleurum	- 11, 12, 13
Mesoscutum	- 1	Upper division of	
Lateral lobe		Metapleuron	- 14
Mesoscutum	- 2	Metapleurum	- 15
Scutellum	- 3	Juxtacoxal area	- 16
Metascutellum	- 4	Propleurum	- 17
Hind margin of		Prepectus	- 18
Metanotum	- 5	Mesosternum	- 19
Tegula	- 6	Front coxa	- 20
Pronotal collar	- 7	Middle coxa	- 21
Pronotal trough	- 8	Hind coxa	- 22
Propleurum	- 9	Propodeum	- 23
Pronotum	- 10	Propodeal spiracle	- 24

CARINAE AND GROOVES

Notaulus	- A	Post pectal carina	- G
Epemia	- B	Juxtacoxal carina	- H
Prepectal carina	- C	Submetapleural carina	- I
Mesopleural fovea	- D	Pleural carina	- J
Mesopleural furrow	- E	Basal transverse carina	- K
Mespoleural suture	- F		

PLATE - IV

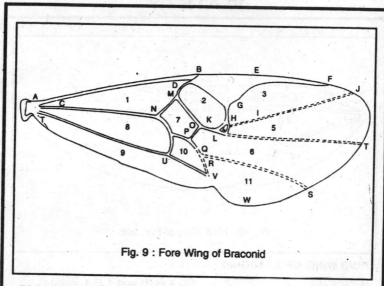

Fig. 9 : Fore Wing of Braconid

FORE WING OF BRACONID

Costa	:	SC + R = AB
Metacarpus	:	R1 = EF
Basal	:	1 M and Rs base = DMN
Radius	:	2 r 2Rs and 3 Rs = GHIJ
Medius	:	M + Cu and 1 A = CN
Cubitus	:	Rs + M, 2M and 3M = KLT
Discoideus	:	Cul and Culd = NPO
Brachium	:	Distal Part 1 A = NM
Subdiscoideus	:	Cula = PQRS
Intercubital	:	1 Rs and r m = HK
Recurrent	:	m - Cu = OP
Nervulus	:	Cu - a = L
Internal	:	2 A = H
Stigma	:	Pts = BGE

CELLS

Medial cell	- 1	Second discoidal cell	- 7
Discocubital cell	- 2	Submedian cell	- 8
Radial cell	- 3	Anal cell	- 9
Areolet	- 4	First brachial cell	- 10
Third cubital cell	- 5	Second brachial cell	- 11
Third discoidal cell	- 6		

PLATE - V

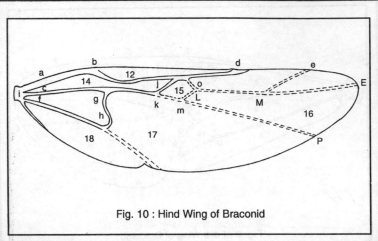

Fig. 10 : Hind Wing of Braconid

HIND WING OF BRACONID

Subcostella	:	SC + R, R and 1 R 1 = abd
Metacarpella	:	2 R l and 3 R l = de
Basella	:	1 r - m = ji
Radiella	:	RS = jL
Mediella	:	M + Cu & IM = Cj
Cubitella	:	2 m & 3 m = KMP
Submediella	:	1A = hf
Intercubitella	:	2 r - m = ml
Nervellus	:	Cu & Cu - a = gh

CELLS

Costellan cell	- 12	Cubitellan cell	- 16
Costellan cell	- 13	Brachiellan cell	- 17
Mediellan cell	- 14	Analan cell	- 18
Basellan cell	- 15		

PLATE - VI

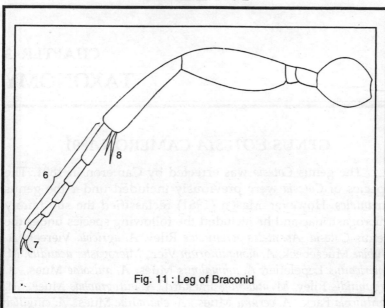

Fig. 11 : Leg of Braconid

LEG OF BRACONID

Coxa	- 1
Trochanter I & II	- 2 & 3
Femur	- 4
Tibia	- 5
Tarsus	- 6
Claw	- 7
Tibial spurs	- 8

CHAPTER 3
TAXONOMY

GENUS *COTESIA* CAMERON 1891

The genus *Cotesia* was errected by Cameron in 1891. The species of *Cotesia* were previously included under the genus *Apanteles*. However, Mason (1981) reclassified the sub family microgastrinae and he included the following species under the genus *Cotesia*. *Apanteles acronyctae* Riley, *A. agricola* Viereck, *A. alypiae* Muesebeck, *A. alonquinorum* Vier., *Microgaster acaudus*, *M. americanus* Lepeletier, *A. ammalonis* Mues. *A. anisotae* Mues., *A. argynnidis* Riley, *M. atalantae* Packard, *A. autographae* Mues., *M. carduicola* Pack., *A. cerurae* Mues., *A. charadrae* Mues., *A. cingiliae* Mues., *A. clisiocampae* Ashmead, *M. congregata* Say, *A. crambi* Weed, *A. cyaniridis* Riley, *A. delicatus* Howard, *A. depressus* Vier., *A. diacrisiae* Gahan, *A. diversus* Muesbeck & Walkley, *A. electrae* Vier., *A. empretiae* Vier., *A. enypiae* Mason, *A. euchaetis* Ash., *A. euphydryidis* Mues., *A fiskei* Vier., *A. flaviconchae* Rilley, *A. flavicornis* Riley, *A. gillettei* Baker, *Ichneumon glomeratus* Linnaeus, *A. gordii* Mues., *A. griffini* Vier., *A. halisidotae* Mues., *M. hallii* Pack., *A. hemileucae* Riley, *A. hesperidivorus* Vier., *A. hyphantriae* Riley, *A. junoniae* Riley, *A. koebelei* Riley, *A. laeviceps* Ash., *A. langei* Mues., *M. limenitidis* Riley, *M. lunatus* Pack; *A lyciae* Mues.., *A. mahoniae* Mason, *M. marginiventris* Cresson., *A. medicaginis* Mues., *M. melanoscelus* Ratzeburg, *A. murtfeldtae* Ash., *A. nemoriae* Ash., *A. nitens* Mues., *A. noctuidiphagus* Mues., *A. obscuricornis* Vier., *A. olenidis* Mues., *A. orobenae* Forbes., *A. parastichtidis* Mues., *A. phobetri* Rohwer., *A. pholisorae* Riley., *A. plathypenae* Mues., *A. podunkorum* Vier., *A. prenidis* Mues., *A. pyralidis* Mues., *A. pyraustae* Vier., *A. pyrophilae* Mues., *A. rubecula* Marshall., *A. rufocoxalis* Riley, *A. schaffneri* Mues., *A. schizurea* Ash., *A. scitulus* Riley, *A. smerithi* Riley, *A. teleae* Mues., *A. theclae* Riley, *A. tmetocerae* Mues., *M. unicolor*

14

Curtis., *A. winkleyi* Vier., *M. xylina* Say, *A. yakutatensis* Ash., *Cotesia flavipes* Cameron, *A. sesamiae* Cameron, *A. pistrinariae* Wilkinson, *A. plutellae* Kurdjimov, *M. ruficrus* Haliday, *A. chrysippi* Vier., *A. flagellator* Wilkn., *A. aluis* Mues., *A. dyerzde* Brethes, *A. kraussi* Mues., *A. mayaguezensis* Vier., *A. ornatricis* Mues. and *A. schini* Mues.

The genus *Cotesia* is largest segregate of old *"Apanteles"* containing 30 per cent to 40 per cent of the species in temperate regions. *Cotesia* is partly displaced ecologically by *Glyptapanteles* containing 10 to 20 per cent of the *"Apanteles"* fauna. The genus is commonest and ubiquitious, comprising 1500 to 2000 species. Most of the species of this genus are gregarious. However, solitary species are also sizable. The characteristics of the cocoon mass plays an important role in identifying the species. Larvae of macrolepidoptera are the hosts for this genus. The genus *Cotesia* is the segregation of group I of Reinhard and Marshall, 'F' of Wilkinson and deSaeger, *glomeratus* and *pistrinariae* groups of Nixon (1965) and *carinatus* subgenus group of Rao (1961). Chalikwar (1974), Chalikwar *et al.* (1982) and recently, Dawale *et al.* (1993) and Sathe *et al.* (1994) have described five species of this genus from India.

Type : *Cotesia flavipes* Cameron 1891.

Synonyms : *Cryptapanteles* Viereck 1990.

Type : (*C. rileyanus* Viereck 1910).

Apanteles congregatus Var. *scitulus* 1881.

Stenopleura Viereck 1911.

Type : *Apanteles sesamiae* Cameron 1906.

COTESIA ANARI SP. NOV.

Female (Fig. 12)

3.29 mm long, excluding ovipositor, fore wing 3.05 mm long, hind wing 2.27 mm long, hind leg 3.46 mm long, ovipositor 0.20 mm long, head, thorax black, abdomen brownish black.

Head

Head circular in dorsal view, black, hairy, 0.75 mm long, 0.62 mm broad; vertex, frons sparsely hairy, hair small, fine; frons show deepening at antennal base; deep punctured face, more or less rectangular and moderately to densely hairy, hair long as compared to vertex and frons; ocelli in triangle, dark, red, shiny, with tubercles; interorbital space 0.12 mm long; frontocellar space 0.050 mm long; eyes large, black, convex, elliptical, shiny, pubescent; interorbital space 0.47 mm long; clypeus yellow, flat, plate like; labrum yellow, semicircular; mandible black, strong, curved.

Antenna (Fig. 43-44)

Antenna 18 segmented, 2.57 mm long including scape and pedicel (Fig. 44), brown, hairy; scape 0.17 mm long; placodes arranged in two longitudinal rows, last antennal segment (Fig. 43) conical, penultimate segment smaller than terminal.

Flagellar formula

$2L/W = 2.6, 8L/W = 2.0, 14L/W = 1.6, L2/14 = 1.6, W2/14 = 1.0$

Thorax

1.22 mm long, black, brownish, anteriorly narrow, posteriorly densely hairy; pronotum large, semicircular, convex; mesonotum punctate; tegulae not depressed, distance between tegulae 0.90 mm and height of thorax at tegulae 0.90 mm; thorax as broad as high; scutellum large and convex; mesoscutellum small, granulated, convex; mesosternum large, plate like, various sulci distinct; Propodeum (Fig. 48) squarish, without areola, 0.33 mm long and 0.87 mm broad, carination suppressed, showing funnel like structure at centre, basal carinae broken, lateral carina without transverse basal branches, median longitudinal carina present,

PLATE - XII

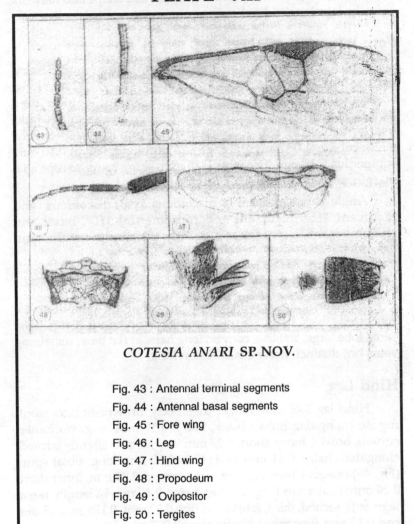

COTESIA ANARI SP. NOV.

Fig. 43 : Antennal terminal segments
Fig. 44 : Antennal basal segments
Fig. 45 : Fore wing
Fig. 46 : Leg
Fig. 47 : Hind wing
Fig. 48 : Propodeum
Fig. 49 : Ovipositor
Fig. 50 : Tergites

oblique transverse carinae forming nipple like shape and network apically, latrolongitudinal carina prominent, spiracles elliptical.

Fore Wing (Fig. 45)

3.05 mm long, straight, transparent, membranous, hairy, narrow basally, broad apically; costa thick, hairy, 1.42 mm long, stigma black, 0.62 mm long, 0.20 mm broad, smaller than metacarpus; metacarpus 0.80 mm long; radial, medial and parallel poorly visible, 1.25 mm, 1.22 mm and 1.15 mm long respectively; mediocubitus 1.07 mm; first anal 1.25 mm long, lateral 0.40 mm; submedius 0.15 mm, nervulus 0.15 mm, wing hairy except anal margin, second radiomedial 0.10 mm long.

Angle between basal & discoideus 110°, discoideus and recurrent 115°, recurrent and radiomedial 110°, basal and radiomedial 85°, radius and cubitus 65° and nervulus and discoideus 67°.

Hind Wing (Fig. 47)

2.27 mm long, small straight, transparent, membranous; subcostella thick, hairy, 1.50 mm long; intercubitella 0.20 mm long; vanal lobe large, leaf like, convex, long hairs at flat base, remaining veins not distinct, nervellus 0.24 mm long.

Hind Leg

Hind leg 3.46 mm, longer than body, brownish; coxa stout, rugose triangular, brown-black, hairy, 0.57 mm long; trochanter curved, brown, hairy, short, 0.27 mm long; femur slightly curved, elongated, hairy, 0.81 mm long; tibia 0.60 mm long; tibial spurs (Fig. 46) unequal, brown, hairy, outer longer, 0.22 mm, inner short, 0.20 mm; basitarsus long, slender, hairy, 0.45 mm in length; tarsal segments, second, third, fourth and fifth 0.22 mm, 0.17mm, 0.15 mm and 0.15 mm long respectively; claw 0.075 mm long.

Abdomen

1.32 mm long, excluding ovipositor, basally narrow, broad apically, dark brown; first abdominal tergite (Fig. 50) half black and half brownish black, rugose, with basal median groove reaching about half the length of it and 'U' shaped notch at middle and 'C' shaped lateral arch at base, 0.30 mm broad, 0.45 mm long;

second tergite 0.30 mm broad and 0.25 mm long, rugose; third tergite yellowish brown, 0.30 mm broad, 0.20 mm long, remaining segments narrow posteriorly; hypopygium 0.4 mm, short; Ovipositor (Fig. 49) considerably longer than sheath, short dagger shaped, hairy, brownish black, 0.20 mm long; ovipositor considerably broader at base and pointed towards tip, ovipositor sheath straight, 0.18 mm long.

Colour

Yellow : abdominal basal segments,

Brown : antenna, coxa, suprs,

Brownish black : abdomen, ovipositor,

Black : head, throax, abdominal last two segments, stigma, hypopygium.

Male

2.5 mm long, smaller than female, same resembling the female except sexual characters.

Cocoon

Gregarious, cottony white, 3.18 mm long, 1.8 mm broad, colony contain 30 to 40 cocoons.

Host

The Anar butterfly larva, *Virachola isocrates* Fabricius.

Host Plant

The Pomegranate, *Punica granatum* (L).

Holotype

Female, India, Maharashtra, Coll. 3.IX.95, Dahiwadi, M.S., Bhoje P.M., antenna, wings, leg, tergites, ovipositor on slide labelled as above.

Paratype

Male 43, female 59, sex ration (M:F) 1:2.2; P.M. Bhoje, Sept. to Feb., same data as above.

Distributional Record

Maharashtra : ♂15, ♀22, Dahiwadi (Satara), 3I.X.95 ♂3, ♀8, Mayani (Satara), 19.XI.96; ♂4, ♀9, Karad (Satara), 19.X.97.

DISCUSSION

This species runs close to *Apanteles* (= *Cotesia*) *euthaliae* Bhatanagar by having propodeum rugose, first abdominal tergite half black in Rao's (1961) key. In Wilkinson's (1928 a) key, it runs close to *Apanteles* (= *Cotesia*) *antipoda* Ashmead by having hind coxa rugose and brownish black white, in Papp's (1987) key, it runs close to *Apanteles* (= *Cotesia*) *pieridis* (Bouche) by having tibial spurs unequal.

However, the species differs from above species by having following characters :

(1)   Antennal terminal segment elongately cone shaped.

(2)   Tergite first with basal median groove reaching about half the length of it and with 'U' shaped notch at middle and 'C' shaped lateral arch at base.

(3)   Ovipositor considerably longer than ovipositor sheath, ovipositor considerably broader at base and pointed towards tip,

(4)   Hypopygium short,

(5)   Propodeum with oblique transverse carinae forming nipple like shape and network apically,

(6)   Angle between radius and cubitus 65°,

(7)   Flagellar formula :
2L/W=2.6, 8L/W=2.0, 14L/W=1.6, L2/14=1.6, W2/14=1.0.

COTESIA ARACHII SP. NOV.

Female (Fig. 13)

3.32 mm in length excluding ovipositor, fore wing 2.90 mm long, hind wing 2.12 mm long, hind leg 3.26 mm long; ovipositor 0.32 mm long; head, thorax black, abdomen yellowish brown except tip, blackish.

Head

Head black, elliptical in dorsal view, hairy pubescent, 0.70 mm long, 0.62 mm broad; vertex punctate; frons sparesly hairy, frons with shallow punctures; face below antennae not prominent, more or less slightly rectangular, squarish, hairy, hairs long, clypeus smooth, semicircular, brownish-black, plate like; labrum roughly rectangular broad, dark brown, convex; ocelli in triangle, shiny, reddish, stud like; interocellar space 0.12 mm, frontocellar space 0.050 mm long; eyes large, convex, pubescent, elliptical, shiny, black; interoribital space 0.35 mm long.

Antenna (Fig. 51, 52)

3.37 mm long, longer than body, filiform, reddish brown, 16 segmented excluding scape and pedicel, hairy, scape (Fig. 51) 0.17 mm long, placodes two to three arranged in longitudinal rows; antennal terminal segment (Fig. 52) sharply conical, terminal second, third and fourth segments increasing in order in length.

Flagellar Formula

2L/W=3.0, 8L/W=4.0, 14L/W=3.5, L2/14=1.3, W2/14=1.5.

Thorax

Black, densely hairy, wider than high, roughly spindle shaped, 1.12 mm long; mesonotum strong punctate, semicircular; scutellum large, flate, plate like, slightly convex; mesocutellum small, convex; mesosternum large, broad, plate like; tegulae slightly depressed, coarse, distance between tegulae 0.96 mm long, height of thorax at tegulae 0.54 mm; Propodeum (Fig. 54) 0.32 mm long and 0.96 mm broad, prominent medio-oblique carinae, strong transverse short carinae, median longitudinal carinae with lateral branches forming network, medio-anterior portion is devoid of network of carinae, spiracles more elliptical.

Fore Wing (Fig. 53)

Fore wing 2.90 mm long, straight, transparent, hairy, except anal margin; costa thick, hairy, 1.35 mm long; stigma black, hairy, 0.60 mm long, 0.20 mm broad; metacarpus 0.75 mm long, stigma smaller than metacarpus, radial, medial and parallel veins distinct 0.97 mm, 1.17 mm, 0.92 mm long respectively, mediocubitus 0.97 mm, first anal 1.15 mm long, lateral 0.37 mm, cubitus 0.15 mm, recurrent vein 0.17 mm, nervulus 0.12 mm long, second radiomedial 0.15 mm long.

Angle between basal and discoideus 115°, discoideus and recurrent 130°, recurrent and radiomedial 100°, basal and radiomedial 70°, radious and cubitus 60° and nervulus and discoideus 90°.

Hind Wing (Fig. 55)

2.12 mm long, transparent, straight, hairy at subcostal margin, subcostella 1.37 mm long, intercubitella 0.12 mm long, remaining veins reduced, vanal lobe leaf like, convex, with tuft of hair at base, nervellus 0.27 mm.

Hind Leg

3.26 mm long, hairy; coxa roughly triangular, brownish black, stout, 0.52 mm long; trochanter short, feeble, slightly curved, yellow, 0.27 mm long; femur long, flattened, stout, hairy, yellow, 0.72 mm long; tibia long, hairy, narrow basally and flat apically, 0.87 mm in length; tibial spurs (Fig. 56) slightly unequal, hairy, pointed, yellowish brown, outer 0.22 mm long, inner short, 0.17 mm long; basitarsus slender, long, densely hairy, 0.19 mm; tarsal segments second, third, fourth and fifth 0.20 mm, 0.15 mm, 0.12 mm and 0.15 mm long respectively, all hairy; claw short, 0.075 mm in length.

Abdomen

Abdomen 1.5 mm long, black dorsally, brown laterally, abdominal tip black, sparsely hairy, smooth; tergites (Fig. 57) black, first tergite narrow basally, broad apically, longer than broad, 0.48 mm long, 0.37 mm broad, wholly black, hairy, plate like, more or less barrel shaped; second tergite rugosopunctate, broader than long, dark medially, brown laterally, 0.50 mm broad, 0.20 mm long; third tergite rugosopunctate, 0.50 mm broad, 0.22 mm long, second and third tergite equal in size, fourth tergite 0.15 mm broad and 0.22 mm long; ovipositor (Fig. 58) pointed, long, without hairs, reddish brown, 0.32 mm long, ovipositor slightly longer than sheath, sheath straight, 0.30 mm long, without hairs.

Colour

Yellowish brown : Spurs, abdomen except tip,

Brownish black : coxa,

Redish brown : Antenna, abdomen laterally, ovipositor,

Black : head, thorax, stigma, abdominal apical few segments.

Male

Male 2.10 mm long, smaller than female, same resembling the female, except sexual characters.

Cocoon (Fig. 42)

Cocoon 2.8 mm long, 1.5 mm broad, cottony white, gregarious, a colony contain 28 cocoons.

Host

Unidentified lepidopterous groundnut semilooper (fig. 30).

Host Plant

The groundnut, *Arachis hypogaea* L.

Holotype

Female, India, Maharashtra, Coll. 2.X.94, Panhala, M.S., Bhoje, P.M., antenna, wings, leg, propodeum, tergites, ovipositor on slide labelled as above.

Paratype

Male 30, female 95, sex ratio (M:F) 1:2.8, same data as above.

Distributional Record

Maharashtra : ♂11, ♀31 Panhala (Kolhapur), 2.X.94; ♂9, ♀23 Shahuwadi (Kolhapur), 6.X.96; ♂10, ♀31 Bidkin (Aurangabad), 13.XI.94.

DISCUSSION

This species runs close to *Apanteles* (= *Cotesia*) *ruidus* Wilkinson in Rao's key (1961) by having third tergite rugose, mesonotum strong and punctate in same part. It also runs close to *Apanteles* (= *Cotesia*) *erionotae* Wilkinson by having propodeum with median longitudinal carina and first tergite whclly black in Wilkinson's key. While, it resembles with *Apanteles* (= *Cotesia*) *salebrosus* Marshall by ovipositor (Papp, 1987) but, it differs from above species by having following characters :

(1)   Terminal antennal segment sharply cone shaped, terminal second, third and fourth segments increasing in order in length,

(2)   Tibial spurs slightly unequal,

(3)   Tergites second and third rugosepunctate.

(4)   Tergite first is with 'V' shaped notch at middle base,

(5)   Propodeum with prominent-median carina with medio-obliqually, prominent carinae forming network. Medio-anterior portion is devoid of network of carinae,

(6)   Ovipositor slightly longer than ovipositor sheath,

(7)   Angle between radius and cubitus 60°.

(8)   Flageller Formula :
2L/W=3.0, 8L/W=4.0, 14L/W=3.5, L2/14=1.3, W2/14=1.5.

PLATE - XIII

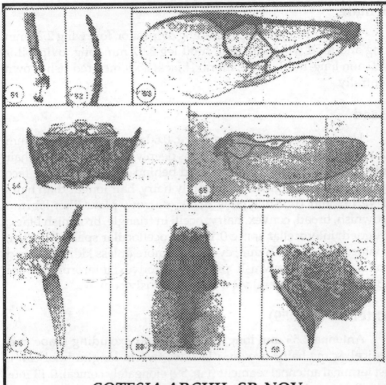

COTESIA ARCHII SP. NOV.

Fig. 51 : Antennal basal segments
Fig. 52 : Antennal terminal segments
Fig. 53 : Fore wing
Fig. 54 : Propodeum
Fig. 55 : Hind wing
Fig. 56 : Leg
Fig. 57 : Tergites
Fig. 58 : Ovipositor

COTESIA BAZARI SP. NOV.

Female

Female 2.86 mm long, excluding ovipositor, fore wing 2.25 mm long and hind wing 1.92 mm, hind leg 3.07 mm long, ovipositor 0.20 mm long, black; head, thorax, black; abdomen reddish brown ventrally.

Head

Head black, more or less circular, 0.60 mm broad and 0.60 mm long; vertex, sparsely punctate, frons deeply sculptured, hairy, hair small, fine; frons slightly depressed behind antennal socket; face more or less rectangular, moderately hairy, hair longer than hairs of vertex and frons; clypeus black, narrow, plate like; labrum brownish, broad, convex, hairy; ocelli in triangle, brownish black, rounded; interocellar space 0.12 mm, ocellocular space 0.17 mm; frontocellar space 0.04 mm; eyes large, more or less kidney shaped from front view, brownish, pubescent, convex; interorbital space 0.37 mm long, in lateral view conspicuously convex.

Antenna (Fig. 59)

Antenna 2.53 mm long, 16 segmented excluding scape and pedicel; scape hairy, brown; placodes two in longitudinal rows, last terminal antennal segment (Fig. 59) elongately conical, 0.13 mm long, 0.04 mm in width, terminal four segments of flagellum more or less equal in length, terminal first 0.13 mm, second 0.11 mm, third 0.11 mm, fourth 0.12 mm in length.

Flagellar formula

2L/W=0.2, 8L/W=1.6, 14L/W=1.2, L2/14=1.5, W2/14=1.00.

Thorax

Thorax black, 0.90 mm in length, densely hairy and ovoid narrow at anterior end and broad posteriorly; pronotum large, convex, semicircular; scutellum convex, large, rugose; scutellar disc smooth and shiny; mesoscutellum small, convex, rugose; tegula slightly depressed due to wing base; distance between tegulae 0.72 mm; height of thorax at tegula 0.60 mm; mesosternum broad,

PLATE - XIV

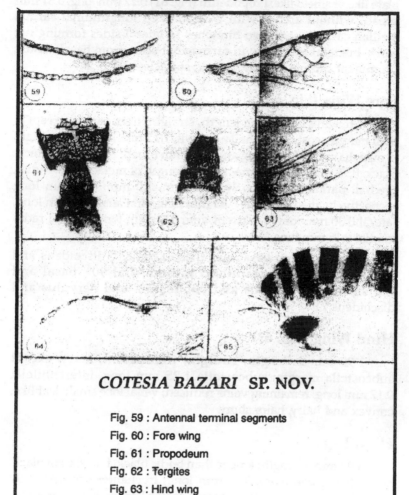

COTESIA BAZARI SP. NOV.

Fig. 59 : Antennal terminal segments

Fig. 60 : Fore wing

Fig. 61 : Propodeum

Fig. 62 : Tergites

Fig. 63 : Hind wing

Fig. 64 : Leg

Fig. 65 : Ovipositor

plate like or shield like; Propodeum (Fig. 61) 0.27 mm long, 0.51 mm broad, without areola, with well marked longitudinal carina, median carina giving two branches to lateral sides forming net work, bilateral symmetry in carinae not seen, from basolaterally prominent carinae gives net work; spiracles elliptical.

Fore Wing (Fig. 60)

Fore wing 2.25 mm in length, straight, transparent, except at anal margin; costa thick, hairy, brown, 1.12 mm long; stigma light brown, hairy, 0.37 mm long and 0.17 mm broad; metacarpus thick, black, 0.75 mm long; stigma half the length of metacarpus; radial, medial, parallel seen poorly, 0.82 mm, 1.0 mm, 0.82 mm long respectively; mediocubitus 0.85 mm long, first anal 0.95 mm long, lateral 0.30 mm long, recurrent vein 0.15 mm long, second radio medial 0.15 mm long.

Angle between basal and discoideus 85°, discoideus and recurrent 110°, recurrent and radiomedial 90°, basal and radiomedial 90°, radius and cubitus 52° and nervulus and discoideus 71°.

Hind Wing (Fig. 63)

1.92 mm in length, straight, transparent, hairy, except subcostella margin; subcostella 1.25 mm long, intercubitella 0.12 mm long; remaining veins reduced; venal lobe small, leaf like, convex and hairy, hairs short.

Hind Leg

3.07 mm in length, longer than body, black, hairy; coxa black, stout, triangular, hairy, 0.45 mm long; trochanter short, slightly curved, hairy, 0.15 mm long; femur redish brown, flat, long, stout, 0.72 mm long; tibia elongated, straight, densely hairy, 0.66 mm long; tibial spurs equal, pointed, hairy, 0.18 mm long; basitarsus moderately long, hairy, 0.30 mm long; tasal segments, second, third, fourth and fifth 0.15 mm, 0.12 mm, 0.10 mm and 0.15 mm long respectively; claw 0.09 mm long, pointed.

Abdomen

1.36 mm in length, excluding ovipositor, hairy, pointed, black, reddish brown ventrally, sparsely hairy, hair arranged roughly parallel on each segment; first and second tergite (Fig. 62) rougose, punctate and hairy; first tergite longer than second, narrow basally, broader apically, first tergite 0.43 mm long and 0.27 mm broad; second tergite 0.29 mm long and 0.30 mm broad, third tergite 0.18 mm long and 0.45 mm broad, smooth, light brown; fourth tergite 0.18 mm long 0.45 mm broad; remaining segments narrow posteriorly to form a abdominal tip, ovipositor (Fig. 65) 0.20 mm long, curved, black, longer than sheath; sheath curved, 0.16 mm long, ovipositor sheath smaller than hind femur, hypopygium light brown, blunt; ovipositor sheath considerably shorter than abdomen.

Colour

Light brown : stigma, spurs, femur,

Reddish brown : ventral of abdomen,

Brown : antenna, eyes,

Black : head, thorax, coxa, dorsal side of abdomen.

Male

Male 2.15 mm long, smaller than female, resembing the female except sexual characters.

Cocoon

Cocoon 2.6 mm long, 1.4 mm in width, cottony white, gregarious.

Host

Unidentified caterpillar (Case Worm) on Bazara,

Larva of *Latoia lepida* Gram. (Fig. 41).

Host Plant

The Bazara, *Pennisetum typhoides* (Rich.).

Holotype

Female, India, Maharashtra, Coll. 11.XII.94, Sarola (Bk), (Osmanabad); M.S., Bhoje P.M., on Bazara, antenna, wings, leg, propodeum, tergites, ovipositor on slide labelled as above.

Paratype

Male 37, Female 78, sex ratio (M:F) 1:2.1, Coll. from Aug. to Nov. same data as above.

Distributional Record

The species is distributed in Marathawada, not reported from Western Maharashtra.

Maharashtra : ♂8, ♀17, Sarola (Bk) (Osmanabad), 11.XII.94; ♂13, ♀31 Bidkin (Aurangabad), 13.XI.94; ♂9, ♀7 Chausala (Beed), 12.XI.95; ♂7, ♀13 Parabhani, 28.XII.97.

DISCUSSION

This species runs close to *Apanteles* (= *Cotesia*) *flavipes* (Cameron) by scutellar disc smooth and shiny, propodeum without areola in Rao's key (1961) and to *Apanteles* (= *Cotesia*) *erionotae* (Wilkinson) by having median well marked carina on propodeum (Wilkinson, 1928).

This species also runs close to *Apanteles errator* Nixon by first tergite (Papp, 1987). However, it differs from above species by having following characters :

(1) Antennal terminal four segments more or less equal in length, terminal segment elongately cone shaped,

(2) Propodeum with dark latero-longitudinal carinae, forming network, and with median longitudinal carina.

(3) Ovipositor curved considerably longer than ovipositor sheath,

(4) Tibial spurs equal,

(5) Third Tergite smooth and light brown,

(6) Eyes in-front view more or less kidney shaped,

(7) Angle between radius and cubitus 52°,

(8) Flagellar formula :
$2L/W=0.2$, $8L/W=1.6$, $14L/W=1.2$, $L2/14=1.5$, $W2/14=1.00$.

COTESIA CHILOI SP. NOV.

Female (Fig. 15)

Female 3.63 mm long excluding ovipositor, fore wing 2.95 mm long, hind wing 2.7 mm long, hind leg 3.65 mm long, ovipositor 0.12 mm long; head, thorax black; abdomen yellowish, blackish at tip.

Head

Head black, elliptical in dorsal view, densely hairy, hairs fine, short and moderately long, 0.78 mm long, 0.65 mm broad, vertex, frons covered by fine hairs, arranged sparsely; frons with shallow punctures sinked at base of antenna, face roughly rectangular, moderately hairy, hair long; clypeus squarish, small plate like, black hairy; labrum dark brown, roughly semicircular, hairy; ocelli in triangle, small, shiny, interocellar space 0.19 mm, frontocellar space 0.050 mm, ocellocular space 0.15 mm; eyes large elliptical, convex, pubescent, shiny, interorbitral distance 0.37 mm long.

Antenna (Fig. 66)

Black, hairy, 3.9 mm long, 16 segmented excluding scape and pedicel, scape hairy; placodes arranged in two or three longitudinal rows; transverse banded; antennal terminal segment (Fig. 66) small, typically conical, slightly tapering to base, 0.9 mm in length, last terminal second 0.6 mm long, third 0.9 mm and fourth 0.11 mm long.

Flagellar formula

2L/W=2.90, 8L/W=2.5, 14L/W=1.5, L2/14=1.7, W2/14=0.95.

Thorax

Thorax 1.55 mm long, black, dorsoventraly compressed, densely hairy, hair moderately long, broad anteriorly, narrow posteriorly; pronotum large, semicircular; tegulae depressed, yellowish brown; scutellum large, convex, punctate, plate like; distance between tagulae 0.50 mm, height of thorax at tegulae 0.48 mm; scutellardisc shiny, convex; mesoscutellum small, convex; mesosturnum large, shield like, various carinae and sulci distinct, sculpture coarse; Propodeum, (Fig. 68) 0.60 mm long and 0.70 mm broad, rough, spiracles elliptical; with areola; median, longitudinal carina short, roughly triangular structure in middle, carination dense, spreading laterally, prominent two lateral carinae arising from basally, two sub-lateral mediobasal carinae join together at anterior forming aerolation and network of carinae, more or less carinae shows bilateral symmetry, a prominent carina arise from basolateral side and goes to anterior along with propodeal lateral regions and forming dense network.

Fore Wng (Fig. 67)

2.95 mm long, straight, transparent, hairy, except anal margin, narrow basally with flat lobe, broad apically; costa thick, hairy, 1.71 mm; stigma blackish-brown, hairy, hayline, 0.60 mm long, 0.20 mm broad; metacarpus 0.75 mm long; radial, medial, parallel poorly distinct and 0.84 mm, 1.35 mm long respectively, mediocubitus 1.05 mm long, first anal 1.30 mm long, basal 0.42 mm; cubitus 0.18 mm; nervulus 0.12 mm; recurrent 0.19 mm long; second radiomedial 0.14 mm long.

Angle between basal and discoideus 95°, discoideus and recurrent 117°, recurrent and radiomedial 115°, basal and radiomedial 72°, radius and cubitus 85° and nervulus and discoideus 90°.

Hind Wing (Fig. 69)

Hind wing 2.70 mm long, transparent, straight, hairy, except subcostal margin; subcostella 1.55 mm long, intercubitella 0.17 mm; nervellus 0.20 mm; radiella 0.17 mm, cubitella 0.85 mm long, basella 0.98 mm long; vanal lobe small, convex, densely hairy at base.

Hind Leg

3.65 mm long; coxa blackish yellow, hairy, roughly triangular, stout, 0.62 mm long; trochanter slightly curved, yellow, short, 0.21 mm long; femur stout, reddish, strong, 0.78 mm long; tibia elongated, straight, narrow basally, broad apically, 0.85 mm long; tibial spur (Fig. 70) equal, hairy, 0.15 mm long; basitarsus slender, long, hairy, 0.45 mm long; tarsal segments second, third, fourth, fifth 0.15 mm, 0.12 mm, 0.12 mm, 0.12 mm, and 0.15 mm long

PLATE - XV

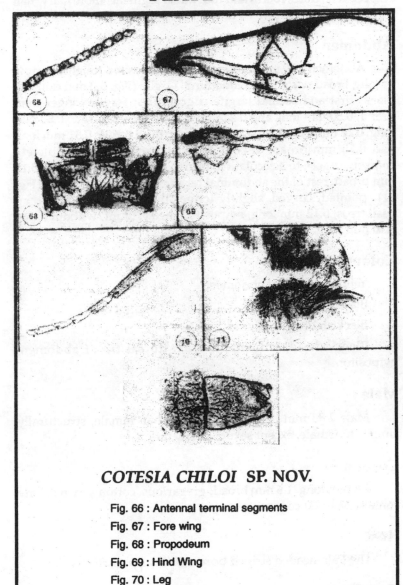

COTESIA CHILOI SP. NOV.

Fig. 66 : Antennal terminal segments
Fig. 67 : Fore wing
Fig. 68 : Propodeum
Fig. 69 : Hind Wing
Fig. 70 : Leg
Fig. 71 : Ovipositor
Fig. 72 : Tergites

respectively; third, fourth and fifth tarsal segments more hairy than other segments; claws 0.08 mm.

Abdomen

Abdomen 1.90 mm long excluding ovipositor, roughly narrow basally, broad posteriorly; abdominal tergite (Fig. 62) mid dorsally black; first and second tergite rugose; first tergite longer than broad, 0.50 mm long and 0.22 mm broad; second tergite 0.30 mm long, 0.28 mm broad, broader than long; third tergite 0.31 mm long and 0.25 mm broad, devoid of sulci, arched and completely coarsely rugose to acicculation; fourth tergite 0.31 mm long, 0.15 mm broad; rest of the abdominal tergites narrow; ovipositor (Fig. 71) pointed, curved, slightly longer than sheath, shorter than basitarsus, 0.12 mm long; ovipositor sheath blunt, without hairs, 0.10 mm long.

Colour

Yellow : lateral of abdomen,

Black : coxa.

Blackish brown : stigma,

Black : head, antenna, thorax, dorsal tip of abdomen, ovipositor.

Male

Male 2.88 mm in length, smaller than female, structurally similar to female, except sexual characters.

Cocoon

2.8 mm long, 1.6 mm broad, gregarious, cottony, each colony contain 35 to 60 cocoons.

Host

The Pale-headed striped borer, *Chilo suppressalis* (Wlk.).

Host Plant

The Paddy, *Oryza sativa* L.

Holotype

Female, India Maharashtra, Coll. Bhoje P.M., 10.X.93, Kolhapur; antenna, wings, leg, propodeum, tergites, ovipositor on slide labelled as above.

Paratype

Male 40, female 72, sex ratio (M:F) 1:1.8, Coll. P.M. Bhoje, Sept. to Feb., same data as above.

Distributional Record

Maharashtra : ♂13, ♀25, Kolhapur, 10.X.93; ♂7, ♀11, Kagal (Kolhapur), 26.IX.94; ♂9, ♀17, Sarola (Bk), 11.XII.94; ♂11, ♀19, Karad (Satara), 25.VIII.96.

DISCUSSION

This species runs close to *Apanteles* (=*Cotesia*) *flavipes* Cameron by having scutellar disc shiny, propodeum carinate and third tergite devoid of sulci (Rao 1961). The species also runs close to *Apanteles chilocida* Viereck in Wilkinson's key by having hind coxa black, thorax compressed dorsoventrally, first tergite at apex broader than at base. In Papp's key it runs clos to *Apantales euchaeties* Ashmaed. However, it differs from above species by having following characters :

(1) Antennal terminal four segments differs in length, last terminal segments typically cone shaped, slightly tapering at base,

(2) Tibial spurs equal in length,

(3) Tegulae yellowish-brown,

(4) Propodeum with two sub-lateral mediobasal carinae, join together at anterior forming aerolation and network of carinae, more or less carinae shows bilateral symmetry. A prominent carina arise from basolateral side goes to anterior along with propodeal lateral regions and forming dense network,

(5) Ovipositor curved, ovipositor sheath without hairs,

(6) Angle between radius and cubitus 85°.

(7) Flagellar formula :
2L/W=2.90, 8L/W=2.5, 14L/W=1.5, L2/14=1.7, W2/14=0.95.

COTESIA JANATI SP. NOV.

Female (Fig. 16)

2.54 mm long, excluding ovipositor, fore wing 2.24 mm long, hind wing 1.8 mm long, hind leg 3.12 mm long; ovipositor 0.4 mm long, head, thorax and abdomen black.

Head

Elliptical, black, densely hairy, hair fine; head 0.52 mm broad, 0.42 mm long; vertex and frons sparsely hairy, hair small fine; frons hardly depressed behind antennal socket; face roughly rectangular and hairy, hairs long as compared to vertex and frons; clypeus smooth not distinctly separated from face, blackish brown, hairy; labrum dark brown, roughly semicircular, hairy; ocelli arranged in triangle, rounded, shiny; interocellar space 0.17 mm; interorbital space 0.45 mm; eyes large, pubescent, convex, shiny, black.

Antenna (Fig. 73)

2.55 mm long, flagellum 16 segmented, scape setaceous, hairy, black, 0.5 mm long; pedicel brown; placodes arranged on flagellum in two to three longitudinal rows; last antennal segment conical, 0.5 mm in length.

Flagellar formula

2L/W=0.2, 8L/W=0.25, 14L/W=1.5, L2/14=0.2, W2/14=0.2.

Thorax

1.22 mm long, braod anteriorly, narrow posteriorly, densely hairy; pronotum large, semicircular, convex; tegula not depressed, black; distance between tegulae 0.69 mm long; height of throax at tegula 0.45 mm; scutellum large, convex, punctate; mesoscutellum small, convex; mesosternum large plate, shield like; Propodeum (Fig. 75) black, rough, with small areola, 0.30 mm long, 0.45 mm broad, rectangular, carinated, carination branched network, arising from both corners at the base of propodeum, and spread anteriorly, carination irregular network, small median carina supported with two lateral carinae at base, spiracles slightly elliptical.

PLATE - XVI

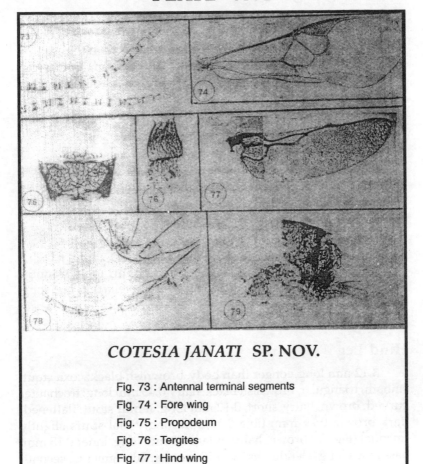

COTESIA JANATI SP. NOV.

Fig. 73 : Antennal terminal segments
Fig. 74 : Fore wing
Fig. 75 : Propodeum
Fig. 76 : Tergites
Fig. 77 : Hind wing
Fig. 78 : Leg
Fig. 79 : Ovipositor

Fore Wing (Fig. 74)

2.24 mm long, straight, transparent, membranous, hairy, narrow basally, broad apically; costa 2.00 mm, subcosta 1.00 mm, mediocubitus 0.75; stigma brown, stigma about equal to radius, stigma hairy, hyaline, 0.51 mm long, 0.15 mm broad; metacarpus 0.50 mm long; radial 0.76 mm; parallel and medial poorly seen; medial 0.90 mm, parallel 0.75 mm, first anal 1 mm long, lateral 0.45 mm, cubitus 0.12 mm, nervulus 0.9 mm long, recurrent 0.3 mm long, bended, 'S' shaped; nervulus 0.10 mm long; second radiomedial 0.15 mm long.

Angle between basal and discoideus 90°, discoideus and recurrent 128°, recurrent and radiomedial 90°, basal and radiomedial 80°, radius and cubitus 70° and nervulus and discoideus 60°.

Hind Wing (Fig. 77)

1.8 mm long, small, straight, transparent, membranous; subcostella thick, hairy, 1.40 mm long; intercubitella 0.15 mm long; anal lobe large, leaf like, convex; nervellus 0.25 mm long, hairy at base; remaining veins indistinct.

Hind Leg

3.12 mm long, longer than body, brownish black; coxa stout, smooth, triangular, brownish black, hairy 0.45 mm long; trochanter curved, brown, hairy, short, 0.12 mm long; femur stout, flattened, dark brown, 0.79 mm; tibia 0.72 mm long; tibial spurs slightly unequal (Fig. 78) brown, hairy outer 0.18 mm long, inner 0.15 mm; basitarsus long, slender, hairy, 0.50 mm; tarsal segments, second, third, fourth and fifth 0.18 mm, 0.15 mm, 0.09 mm and 0.09 mm long respectively, claw 0.03 mm long.

Abdomen

1.8 mm long excluding ovipositor, basally narrow, apically broad, blackish-brown; first tergite (Fig. 76) rugose, narrow at base, anterior half black, 0.30 mm long, 0.19 mm broad, second tergite apically half brownish-yellow, 0.30 mm broad, 0.19 mm long, smooth; third tergite 0.20 mm long, 0.31 mm broad; ovipositor (Fig. 79) short, hairy, dark brown, 0.4 mm long, curved, longer than sheath; sheath (Fig. 79) without hairs, straight, smaller than femora, sparsely punctate apically.

Colour

Brown : stigma,

Brownish black : coxa, ovipositor, abdomen,

Black : head, thorax, antenna.

Male

2.10 mm long, smaller than female; structurally same as female except sexual characters.

Cocoon

Silvery, solitary, 2.5 mm long, 1.0 mm broad (Fig. 29).

Host

The caster semilooper, *Achea janata* L. (Fig. 32).

Host Plant

The caster, *Ricinus communis* L.

Holotype

Female, India, Maharashtra, Coll. Bhoje P.M., 11.XII.94, Sarola (Bk) Osmanabad, M.S., antenna, wings, hind leg, propodeum, tergites, ovipositor on slide labelled as above.

Paratype

Male 31, Female 125, sex ratio (M:F) 1:4, Coll. Bhoje P.M., Oct. to Jan., same data as above.

Distributional Record

Maharashtra : ♂6, ♀30, Sarola (Bk), (Osmanabad), 11.XII.94; ♂3, ♀8, Parbhani, 28.XII.97; ♂2, ♀5, Bidkin (Aurangabad), 13.XI.94; ♂8, ♀38, Shahagad (Jalana), 6.VIII.94; ♂2, ♀5, Chausala (Beed), 12.XI.95; ♂10, ♀39, Murud (Latur), 19.X.97.

DISCUSSION

The species runs close to *Apanteles brachmiae* Bhatnagar in Rao's key by having scape black, stigma brownish, R1, more or less equal to stigma, hind leg dark brown and stigma hyaline. This species also runs close to *Apanteles (=Cotesia) taprobanae* Cameron by having propodeum with distinct transverse basal carinae and second tergite without lateral sulci (Wilkinson, 1928 a). In Papp's (1987) key this species runs close to *Apanteles abjectus* Marshall by ovipositor. However, it differs from above species by having following characters :

(1) Ovipositor length less than femur,

(2) Scape setaceous,

(3) Antenna with two to three placodes in longitudinal rows,

(4) Tibial spurs slightly unequal,

(5) Ovipositor sheath sparsely punctate apically,

(6) Angle between radius and cubitus 70°,

(7) Flagellar formula :
2L/W=2, 8L/W=0.25, 14L/W=1.5, L2/14=0.2, W2/14=0.2.

COTESIA MANGIFERI SP. NOV.

Female (Fig. 17)

Female 3.57 mm in length excluding ovipositor, fore wing 2.90 mm long, hind wing 2.12 mm long, hind leg 3.07 mm; ovipositor 0.32 mm long; head, thorax black, abdomen deep brown.

Head

Head black, elliptical in dorsal view, hairy, pubescent, minutely punctate, 0.52 mm long, 0.60 mm broad; vertex, frons sparsely hairy with fine hair, frons sinked at antennal base, slightly punctate, face roughly rectangular, hairy with long hair; clypeus brown, smooth plate, labrum broad and more circular; ocelli in triangle, interocellar space 0.13 mm, intercorbital space 0.29 mm long; frontocellar space 0.075 mm; eyes large, convex, pubescent, elliptical, shny, black.

Antenna (Fig. 80, 81)

Antenna reddish brown, 18 segmented including scape and pedicel; scape 0.16 mm long; flagellum 3.00 mm long, hairy, longer than body, placodes two in ranks, terminal antennal segment elongated and conical 0.13 mm long, terminal four segments more or less equal (Fig. 80), terminal third segment considerably smaller than fourth.

Flageller Formula

2L/W=0.2, 8L/W=0.2, 14L/W=0.12, L2/14=0.2, W2/14=1.3.

Thorax

Thorax black, densely hairy, roughly spindle shaped, 1.65 mm long; scutellum, mesoscutellum rugose, scutellum large plate like, punctate, slightly convex, mesocutellum small convex; mesosternum large, broad elliptical; scutellum, mesoscutellum rugose; tegulae black; distance between tegulae 0.90 mm; height of thorax at tegula 0.60 mm; mesonotum rugose; scutellar disc convex; Propodeum (Fig. 83) 0.30 mm long and 0.60 mm broad, rugose; without areola, two lateral carinae arises from the latero basally giving side branches and forming network, lateral carinae darker than middle, sublateral and lateral carinae present, spiracles rounded.

Fore Wing (Fig. 82)

Fore wing 2.90 mm long, straight, transparent, hairy except anal margin; costa thick, hairy, 1.55 mm long; stigma reddish brown, hairy, 0.60 mm long, 0.15 mm broad; metacarpus 0.75 mm long, metacarpus longer than stigma; radial 0.80 mm; medial and parallel veins indistinct, 1.68 mm, 0.90 mm long respectively; mediocubitus 0.90 mm, first anal 1.05 mm; lateral 0.45 mm, cubitus 0.20 mm; recurrent vein 0.17 mm, nervulus 0.12 mm long, second medial 0.15 mm long, radial well marked.

Angle between basal and discoideus 95°, recurrent and radiomedial 100°, basal and radio medial 86°, radius and cubitus 77° and nervulus and discoideus 61°.

Hind Wing

Hind wing 2.12 mm long, transparent, straight, subcostal margin hairy; subcostella 1.05 mm long, intercubitella 0.12 mm long, remaining veins reduced or absent; venal lobe leaf like, convex, with tuft of hair at base uniformly, intercubitella absent, nervellus 0.27 mm.

Hind Leg

Hind leg 3.07 mm long, brown, hairy; coxa deeply brown, roughly triangular, brownish black, stout, 0.48 mm; trochanter short, feeble, slightly curved, yellow, 0.18 mm; femur long flattened, stout hairy, yellow, 0.60 mm long; tibia long, hairy, narrow basally, flat apically, 0.78 mm in length; tibial spurs (Fig. 85) unequal, hairy, pointed, outer 0.15 mm long, inner 0.12 mm long; basitarsus slender, densely hairy, 0.39 mm long; tarsal segments, second, third, fourth and fifth 0.18 mm, 0.12 mm, 0.15 mm and 0.12 mm respectively, all hairy; claw short, 0.07 mm in length.

Abdomen

Abdomen 2.07 mm in length, thrice the length of ovipositor sheath, black, dorsally, brown laterally and ventrally, abdominal tip black, entire abdomen sparsely hairy, hair arranged roughly

PLATE - XVII

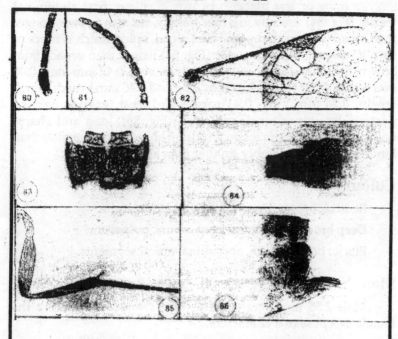

COTESIA MANGIFERI SP. NOV.

Fig. 80 : Antennal basal segments

Fig. 81 : Antennal terminal segments

Fig. 82 : Fore wing

Fig. 83 : Propodeum

Fig. 84 : Tergites

Fig. 85 : Leg

Fig. 86 : Ovipositor

parallel to one another, sculptured rough and carinated; abdominal tergites more or less blackish brown in colour, first abdominal tergite (Fig. 84) apically, narrow basally, reddish brown, longer than broad 0.51 mm long, 0.37 mm broad, apical notch is more or less 'V' shaped, second tergite (Fig. 84) longer than broad, faint brown, medially dark brown, apically smooth, 0.42 mm long, 0.40 mm broad, third tergite 0.24 mm long and 0.40 mm broad, fourth tergite 0.26 mm long, 0.41 mm broad; rest tergites narrow posteriorly; ovipositor deep brown (Fig. 86), long and sharp, without hairs, 0.32 mm long; ovipositor sheath hairy, smaller than hind femora, considerably smaller than abdomen.

Colour

Reddish brown : antenna, stigma, first tergite,

Deep brown : abdomen, coxa, spurs, ovipositor,

Black : head, thorax, abdominal apical segments.

Male

Male 2.55 mm long, smaller than female, resembling the female except sexual characters.

Cocoon

Cocoon 3.2 mm long, 1.00 mm broad, cottony white, gregarious, a colony contain about 40 cocoons.

Host

The Hairy caterpillar on mango, *Inderbela tetraonis* Moore.

Host Plant

The Mango, *Mangifera indica*. (L.).

Holotype

Female, India, Maharashtra, Coll. 29.XII.93, Warananagar, M.S., Bhoje P.M., on Mango, antenna, wings, leg, propodeum, tergites, ovipositor on slide labelled as above.

Paratype

Male 51, female 112; sex ratio (M:F) 1:2.1; Coll. from Oct. to Dec., same data as above.

Distributional Record

Maharashtra : ♂3, ♀7 Warananagar (Kolhapur), 29.XII.93; ♂9, ♀21 Kalamba (Kolhapur), 4.XII.94; ♂7, ♀14 Malakapur (Kolhapur), 24.XI.96; ♂8, ♀15 Surul (Satara), 19.X.97; ♂6, ♀14 Chakan (Pune), 13.X.94; ♂5, ♀9 Pali (Satara), 11.XII.94; ♂6, ♀12 Phalatan (Satara) 22.X.95.

DISCUSSION

This species runs close to *Apanteles* (=*Cotesia*) *papillionis* Viereck by having no areola and first tergite some what reddish brownish, second tergite smooth apically (Rao, 1961); it also runs close to *Apanteles* (=*Cotesia*) *belippae* in Wilkinson's (1928) Key. This species also resembles with *A.* (=*Cotesia*) *salteter* (Thunberg) by terminal 3 segments of antenna in Papp's key. However, it differs from above species by having following characters :

(1) Antennal terminal segments more or less equal, third is considerably smaller than fourth,

(2) Propodeum with median carina, two sublateral carinae and pair of lateral carinae forming network,

(3) Entire abdomen sparsely hairy, first tergite with apical notch 'V' shaped.

(4) Ovipositor sheath considerably smaller than abdomen and with hairs,

(5) Metacarpus longer than stigma,

(6) Angle between radius and cubitus 77°,

(7) Flageller formula :
2L/W=0.2, 8L/W=0.2, 14L/W=0.12, L2/14=0.2, W2/14=1.3.

COTESIA PARANARI SP. NOV.

Female (Fig. 18)

Female 3.57 mm in length excluding ovipositor, forewing 2.10 mm long, hind wing 1.80 mm long, hind leg 2.8 mm long, ovipositor 0.17 mm long; head, thorax, black; abdomen, yellowish brown.

Head

Head more or less circular in front view, black, pubescent, 0.67 mm long, and 0.60 mm broad; vertex, frons sparsely punctate, hairy, hair small in size; frons depressed due to anternnal socket; face some what circular, moderately hairy; clypeus black, narrow; labrum brownish broad, semicircular, hairy; ocelli in triangle, brownish, black rounded, shiny; interocellar space 0.20 mm, frontocellar space 0.044 mm, interorbital space 0.29 mm; eyes brownish black, pubescent, convex, ovoid.

Antenna (Fig. 87, 88)

Black, flagellum 16 segmented, 2.64 mm long excluding scape (Fig. 87) and pedicel; scape black, hairy; scape 0.14 mm; flagellum without band, placodes arranged in two to three longitudinal rows, terminal segment (Fig. 88) conical, 0.12 mm long, first four terminal segments are more or less equal in a length, fifth and sixth considerably longer than four terminal segments (Fig. 88).

Flagellar Formula

2L/W=0.2, 8L/W=0.2, 14L/W=0.13, L2/14=1.5, W2/14=1.

Thorax

Thorax black, 1.0 mm long in length, densely hairy and oviod, narrow anteriorly and broad posteriorly, thorax wider between tegulae than high; distance between tegulae 0.75 mm; height of thorax at tegula 0.90 mm; pronotum large, convex, semicircular; scutellum convex; mesoscutellum small; scutellum, mesoscutellum punctate, small, convex; tegulae slightly depressed due to wing base, reddish brown; mesosturnum broad plate, shied like, sculptured; Propodeum (Fig. 90) rugose, 0.44 mm long, 0.75 mm broad, carinae in network, short median carina bifurcated apically, two submedian carinae arise from the base, a prominent laterolongitudinal carina arise from base giving side branches and forming network, central protion of propodeum with light carination; spiracles circular.

Fore Wing (Fig. 89)

Fore wing 2.10 mm in length, straight, transparent, hairy except at anal margin; costa is thick, hairy, brown, 1.12 mm long; stigma yellowish black, hyaline, hairy, 0.30 mm long, 0.15 mm broad; metacarpus thick, black, 0.72 mm, longer than stigma; radial, medial and parallel not so distinct, 0.78 mm, 0.92 mm and 0.78 respectively; radius longer than stigma, first anal 0.85 mm long, lateral 0.25 mm, cubitus 0.10 mm, nervulus 0.10 mm long, recurrent vein 0.12 mm long and second radiomedial 0.12 mm long.

Angle between basal & discoideus 90°, discoideus & recurrent 120°, recurrent & radiomedial 94°, basal & radiomedial 99°, radius & cubitus 76° and nervulus & discoideus 60°.

Hind Wing

Hind wing 1.80 mm in length, straight, transparent, hairy except subcostellar margin, subcostella 1.22 mm long, intercubitella 0.10 mm, remaining veins indistinct, vanal lobe small, leaf like, convex and hairy, nervellus 0.19 mm.

Hind Leg

Hind leg 2.8 mm in length, shorter than body, black hairy; coxa stout, dull, blackish, rugulose, hairy, 0.48 mm long; trochanter short, slightly curved, hairy, 0.14 mm long; femur flat, long, stout, 0.58 mm long, dark brown in colour, tibia elongate, straight, densely hairy, 0,78 mm long; tibial spurs unequal, pointed, hairy outer 0.12 mm in length, inner 0.10 mm long; basitarsus moderately long, hairy, 0.35 mm long; tarsal segment second, third, fourth and fifth 0.13 mm, 0.10 mm, 0.08 and 0.09 long respectively; claw 0.07 mm long, pointed.

Abdomen

Abdomen 2.04 mm in length, excluding ovipositor, black,

oviod, broad basely and pointed posteriorly, sparsely, hairy; first tergite (Fig. 92) oblong, longer than broad, 0.51 mm long, 0.36 mm broad, basal half smooth, shiny with strong acciculation laterally, apical half rugose, with 'V' shaped notch at middle; second tergite broader than long, 0.32 mm broad, 0.26 mm long, hairy, rugulose, third tergite 0.28 mm long, 0.34 mm broad, smooth; fourth tergite 0.27 mm long, 0.33 mm broad; remaining segments narrow posteriorly; ovipositor (Fig. 93) black, pointed, 0.17 mm long, curved, with few hairs on tip, lightly longer than sheath, ovipositor sheath smaller than hind femora, brown, 0.30 mm in length; hypopygium light yellow in colour.

Colour

Yellowish black : stigma

Brownish black : eyes,

Black : head, thorax, coxa, ovipositor, antenna and abdominal last three segments.

Male

Male 2.10 mm long, smaller than female, similar to female except sexual characters.

Cocoon (Fig. 28)

Cocoon 3.0 mm long, 1.65 mm broad, yellowish white, gregarious, a colony contain about 20 cocoons.

Host

The Rice skipper, *Parnara mathias* Fab.

Host Plant

The Maize, *Zea mays* Linn.

Holotype

Female, India, Maharashtra, Coll. 27.XI.94, Islampur; M.S., Bhoje P.M., antenna, wings, leg, propodeum, tergites, ovipositor on slide labelled as above.

PLATE - XVIII

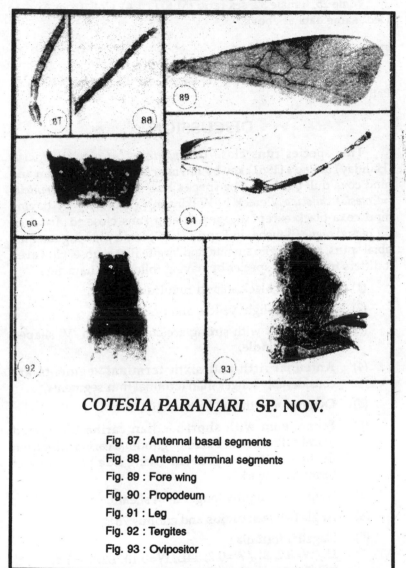

COTESIA PARANARI SP. NOV.

Fig. 87 : Antennal basal segments
Fig. 88 : Antennal terminal segments
Fig. 89 : Fore wing
Fig. 90 : Propodeum
Fig. 91 : Leg
Fig. 92 : Tergites
Fig. 93 : Ovipositor

Paratype

Male 25, female 32, sex ratio (M:F) (1:1.4), Coll. from Aug. to Dec., same data as above.

Distributional Record

Maharashtra : ♂13, ♀16 Islampur, 27.XI.94; ♂12, ♀16 Pethnaka, 17.XI.96.

DISCUSSION

This species runs close to *Apanteles (=Cotesia) ruficrus* (Haliday) in Rao's (1961) key by having carinate propodeum and hind coxa dull blackish. The species also runs close to *Apanteles (=Cotesia) chilocida* Viereck in Wilkinson's (1928) key by having hind coxa black except at apex. It also runs close to *Apanteles (=Cotesia) cague* (Bouche) in Papp's (1987) key by having unequal tibial spurs, third tergite smooth and tergite first rugose. However, it differs from above species by having following characters:

(1) Coxa dull blackish and rugulose,

(2) Hypogium light yellow and pointed,

(3) Tergite first with strong acciculation with 'V' shaped notch at middle,

(4) Antennal fifth and sixth terminal segments are considerably longer than terminal four segments,

(5) Ovipositor with few hairs on tip,

(6) Propodeum with short median carina bifurcated apically. Prominent laterolongitudinal carina arise from the base of the propodeum giving side branches and forming network,

(7) Ovipositor slightly longer than sheath,

(8) Angle between radius and cubitus 76°,

(9) Flagellar formula :
2L/W=0.2, 8L/W=0.2, 14L/W=0.13, L2/14=1.5, W2/14=1.

COTESIA SUNFLOWARI SP. NOV.

Female (Fig. 19)

3.09 mm in length, excluding ovipositor, fore wing 2.77 mm long; hind wing 2.27 mm long, hind leg 3.06 mm, ovipositor 0.17 mm long; head, thorax black, abdomen brownish, shiny with mid-dorsal black strip.

Head

Roughly circular in dorsal view, dark back, hairy, 0.72 mm long, 0.65 mm broad; vertex, frons sparsely hairy, hair short, fine; frons shiny, with deepening at antennal base; vertex with shallow punctures; face more or less rectangular, moderately hairy, with long hair; clypeus small, convex plate like; labrum broad, brown, plate like, somewhat slightly convexly bended; ocelli in triangle, shiny, rounded; interocellar space 0.12 mm long; frontocellar space 0.050 mm long; eyes large convex, shiny, pubescent, black; interorbital space 0.32 mm long.

Antenna (Fig. 94, 95)

Antenna 18 segmented, 3.19 mm long, brown, hairy, placodes arranged in two to four longitudinal rows, last terminal segment (Fig. 95) short conical, 0.9 mm long; scape 0.17 mm long.

Flagellar formula

2L/W=3.0, 8L/W=3.0, 14L/W=2.5, L2/14=1.8, W2/14=1.5.

Thorax

Thorax 0.97 mm long, black, densely hairy, narrow anteriorly, broad posteriorly; pronotum large, semicircular; scutellardisc large, shallowly punctate, convex; mesoscutellum small, convex; mesosternum large, broad plate like; tegulae depressed due to wing base, length between tegulae 0.90 mm, height of thorax at tegulae 0.54 mm; Propodeum (Fig. 97) without areola, 0.32 mm long, 1.0 mm broad, spiracles elliptical, strong median carinae and transverse carinae on propodeum forming network, median longitudinal carinae with lateral carinae, forming network, two lateral longitudinal carinae, basal carinae present.

Fore Wing (Fig. 96)

2.5 mm long, transparent, membranous, lobed, apically broad, baselly narrow; stigma light brown, hairy, 0.5 mm long, 0.5 mm broad; costa 1.5 mm, subcosta 1.00, mediocubitus 0.87 mm, metacarpus 1.2 mm, subdiscoideus 0.8 mm, submedius 0.10 mm, lateral 0.4 mm, nervulus 0.17 mm, recurrent 0.1 mm long, radial 0.83 mm, medial 1.02 mm long, parallel 0.70 mm long, first anal 0.20 mm long, second radiomedial 0.18 mm long.

Angle between basal & discoideus 115°, discoideus & recurrent 130°, recurrent & radiomedial 110°, basal & radio medial 70°, radius & cubitus 60° and nervulus & discoideus 64°.

Hind Wing (Fig. 98)

Hind wing 2.27 mm long, straight, transparent, hairy, membranous; subcostella thick, basally hairy, 1.52 mm long; intercubitella poorly visible, 0.19 mm; radialla, mediallla, cubitella poorly visible 0.17 mm, 1.15 mm, 0.90 mm respectively; anal lobe comparatively large, convex, leaf like and hairy; nervellus 0.25 mm.

Hind Leg

3.06 mm brownish yellow, hairy; coxa black, roughly triangular, stout punctate, 0.52 mm long, trochanter slightly curved, brown 0.13 mm long; femur short, straight, flattened, 0.67 mm long; tibia longest part of leg, slender straight, narrow basally, flat apically, 0.67 mm long; tibial spurs (Fig. 99) unequal, hairy, pointed, outer 0.22 mm long, inner 0.21 mm long; basitarsus slender, straight, 0.42 mm long; tarsal segments, second, third, fourth and fifth short, densely hairy, 0.20 mm, 0.17 mm, 0.15 mm 0.12 mm long respectively; claw short, hairy 0.01 mm long.

Abdomen

1.48 mm in length excluding ovipositor, ovoid, sparsely hairy, dark brown, black strip dorsally; first tergite (Fig. 100) black, with fine hairs, rugose, longer than broad, 0.60 mm long, 0.22 mm broad; narrow basally broad apically; second tergite black, strip on mid-dorsal region, brownish laterally, broader than long, 0.45 mm broad, 0.30 mm long, third tergite blackish brown mid-dorsally, brownish laterally, smooth, 0.45 mm broad, 0.30 mm long, broader than long, second and third tergites equal in size, ovipositor

(Fig. 101) pointed, brownish black, strong, 0.17 mm long, ovipositor sheath and ovipositor equal in length; ovipositor sheath straight, without hairs, brownish black.

Colour

Brown : antenna,

Brownish black : abdomen, stigma,

Black : head, thorax, mid dorsal strip on abdomen.

Male

2.97 mm long, smaller than female, same resembling the female except sexual characters.

Cocoon

Cottony white, 3.15 mm long, 2.1 mm broad, gregarious, colony contain 38 to 45 cocoons.

Host

The Bihar hairy caterpillar, *Spilosoma obliqua* (Walk.) (Fig. 36).

Host Plant

The Sunflower, *Helianthus annuus* L.

Holotype

Female, India, Maharashtra, Coll.12.XI.95, Gaganbawda, M.S., Bhoje P.M., antenna, wings, leg, propodeum, tergites, ovipositor on slide, labelled as above.

Paratype

Male 49, female 85, sex ratio (M:F) 1:1.7, Coll. P.M. Bhoje, from Sept. to Dec. same data as above.

Distributional Record

Maharashtra : ♂17, ♀12, Gaganbawada (Kolhapur), 26.X.195; ♂16, ♀19, Warnanagar (Kolhapur), 19.XII.93; ♂16, ♀22, Kalamba (Kolhapur), 3.X.93.

PLATE - XIX

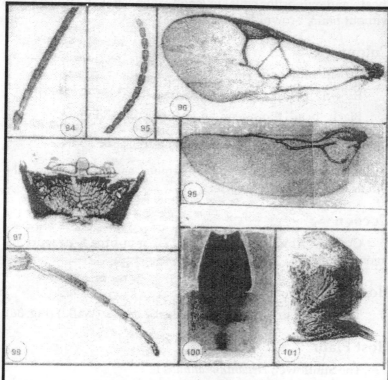

COTESIA SUNFLOWARI SP. NOV.

Fig. 94 : Antennal basal segments
Fig. 95 : Antennal terminal segments
Fig. 96 : Fore wing
Fig. 97 : Propodeum
Fig. 98 : Hind Wing
Fig. 99 : Leg
Fig. 100 : Tergites
Fig. 101 : Ovipositor

DISCUSSION

This species runs close to *Apanteles (=Cotesia) cirphicola* Bhatnagar in Rao's key by having scutellardisc large and shallowly punctate. In Wilkinson's key it runs close to *Apanteles chilocida* Viereck by having hind coxa black while in Papp's key it runs close to *Apanteles (=Cotesia) cajae* Bouche by having tibial spurs unequal. However, it differs from above species by having following characters :

(1) Ovipositor and ovipositor sheath equal in length,

(2) Strong median carina and transverse carinae on propodeum forming network,

(3) Median black strip on tergite second and third,

(4) Stigma smaller than metacarpus,

(5) Angle between radius and cubitus 60°,

(6) Flagellar formula :
2L/W=30, 8L/W=3.0, 14L/W=2.5, L2/14=1.8, W2/14=1.5.

COTESIA TUSKI SP. NOV.

Female (Fig. 20)

Female 3.00 mm long excluding ovipositor, blackish brown, fore wing 2.70 mm long, hind wing 2.10 mm, hind leg 3.10 mm long, ovipositor 0.3 mm long; head, thorax black; abdomen citrunous brown.

Head

Head black, elliptical in dorsal view, densely hairy, hair fine, short, 0.60 mm long and 0.57 mm broad; vertex, frons, covered by fine hairs; frons depressed due to antennal socket; face roughly rectangular, moderately hairy; clypeus squarish, plate like, black, hairy; labrum dark brown, roughly semicircular hairy; ocelli in triangle; interocellar space 0.15 mm; frontocellar space 0.069 mm; eyes large elliptical, convex, pubescent, shiny; interorbital space 0.33 mm long.

Antenna (Fig. 102, 103)

Antenna 18 segmented, black, hairy, flagellum 3.00 mm long, scape and pedicel (Fig. 102) black, smooth; placodes arranged in two longitudinal rows; terminal segment (Fig. 103) small, conical 0.6 mm long; scape 0.17 mm long; terminal four segments: first 0.6 mm long, second 0.8 long, third 0.9 mm long and fourth 0.9 mm long; last terminal segment elongately cone shaped and rest segments more or less equal in length but reduced in their width considerably.

Flagellar formula

2L/W=2.3, 8L/W=1.6, 14L/W=2.0, L2/14=0.3, W2/14=1.3.

Thorax

Thorax 1.10 mm long, slightly narrow basally, broad apically, black in colour, densely hairy, smooth; tegulae not depressed, black, distance between tegulae 0.62 mm; height of thorax at tegulae 0.75 mm; pronotum large, convex; mesoscutellum small, punctate, convex; scutellum large, convex; mesosternum large plate, shield like, surface carinated; Propodeum (Fig. 105) rectangular, sparsely punctate, broader than long, 0.30 mm long, 0.54 mm broad; spiracles rounded; propodeum invariably rugose, without areolation, highly carinated median carina prominent, laterolongitudinal carina very prominent, irregular carination forming network.

Fore Wing (Fig. 104)

Fore wing 2.70 mm long, straight, transparent, elongated hairy, except anal margin; costa 1.26 mm long thick, reddish brown, hairy; stigma black with reddish spot, 0.51 mm long, 0.18 mm broad, stigma smaller than radius; metacarpus 0.60 mm long, metacarpus more or less equal to stigma; radial, 0.30 mm long, medial 1.00 mm discoideous 0.45 mm long, parallel 0.78 mm, mediocubitus 0.80 mm long, basal vein 0.36 mm long, first recurrent vein 0.30 mm long, first anal 0.5 mm long, nervulus 0.15 mm long and second radiomedial 0.12 mm long.

Angle between basal & discoideus 95°, discoideus & recurrent 127°, recurrent & radiomedial 86°, basal & radiomedial 90°, radius & cubitus 75° and nervulus & discoideus 70°.

Hind Wing (Fig. 106)

2.10 mm long, straight, transparent, hairy; subcostella 1.20 mm long, thick; metacarpella 0.53 mm, nervellus 0.15 mm, basella 0.15 mm; medialla, cubitella poorly visible, 0.97 mm and 90 mm long respectively; intercubitella 0.15 mm long; venal lobe convex, leaf like and hairy.

Hind Leg

3.10 long, longer than body, coxa reddish brown, smooth, remaining segments yellowish brown; coxa, femur smooth, coxa stout, triangular, 0.42 mm long, dull to black at base; trochanter, curved, weak, brown, short, 0.25 mm long; femur yellowish brown, smooth, 0.81 mm long, spindle shaped; tibia 0.69 mm long; basitarsus slender, 0.36 mm long; tibial spurs (Fig. 107) unequal, outer 0.18 mm, inner 0.15 mm long; tarsal segment second, third, fourth and fifth 0.18 mm, 0.12 mm, 0.10 mm and 0.10mm long respectively; claw 0.075 mm long.

PLATE - XX

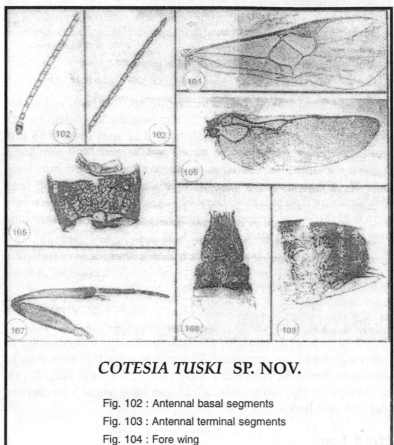

COTESIA TUSKI SP. NOV.

Fig. 102 : Antennal basal segments
Fig. 103 : Antennal terminal segments
Fig. 104 : Fore wing
Fig. 105 : Propodeum
Fig. 106 : Hind wing
Fig. 107 : Leg
Fig. 108 : Tergites
Fig. 109 : Ovipositor

Abdomen

1.45 mm long excluding ovipositor, black dorsally, citrunus ventrally; hairy, tapering at anterior region, broader at posterior portion; first tergite with vestigial notch in middle at the base, rugulose and length greater than second tergite, first tergite (Fig. 108) longer than broad, rugulose, 0.43 mm long, 0.22 mm broad, dark brown in colour; second tergite broader than long, longer than third, longitudinal linings present, rugulose, 0.18 mm long, 0.30 mm broad; third tergite smooth, broader than first and second tergite, 0.15 mm long, 0.36 mm broad; ovipositor (Fig. 109) 0.12 mm long, pointed, curved, dark brown at base, yellowish brown at the tip; ovipositor sheath equal to ovipositor, smaller than femur, sparsely punctate, pointed.

Colour

Citrunus brown : abdomen,

Reddish brown : stigma, coxa,

Black : head, antenna, thorax, mid-dorsal of abdomen.

Male

2.35 mm long, slightly smaller than female, other characters similar to female, except sexual.

Cocoon

Cottony white, gregarious, 3.00 mm long, 1.50 mm broad, colony contain 12 cocoons.

Host

The Tusscuk caterpillar, *Euproctis lunata* (Walker) (Fig. 34).

Host Plant

The Pigeon pea, *Cajanus cajan* (Millusp).

Holotype

Female, India, Maharashtra, Coll. 30.X.94, Islampur, M.S., Bhoje, P.M., antenna, wings, leg, propodeum, tergites, ovipositor on slide labelled as above.

Paratype

Male 33 female 42, sex ratio (M:F), 1:1.2, Coll. from Aug. to Sept., same data as above.

Distributional Record

Maharashtra : ♂13, ♀15, Islampur (Sangli), 30.X.94; ♂9, ♀11, Karad (Satara), 14.XII.97; ♂11, ♀6, Dahiwadi (Satara), 31.X.95.

DISCUSSION

This species resembles with *Apanteles* (=*Cotesia*) *ruficrus* (Haliday) by having third tergite smooth and coxa dull to black in Rao's key. It also resembles with *Apanteles chilocida* Viereck in Wilkinson's key by hind coxa black. It also resembles with *Apanteles callimone* Nixon by having tibial spurs unequal in Papp's key. However it differs from above species by having following characters :

(1) Propodeum without areola, with strong basolateral longitudinal carinae, median carina present,

(2) Metacarpus more or less equal to stigma,

(3) Tibial spurs unequal,

(4) First tergite with vestigial notch in middle at the base, rugulose and length greater than second tergite,

(5) Second tergite longer than third, rugulose,

(6) Ovipositor and ovipositor sheath equal, ovipositor smaller than femur,

(7) Angle between radius and cubitus 75°,

(8) Flagellar formula :
2L/W=2.3, 8L/W=1.6, 14L/W=2.0, L2/14=0.3, W2/14=1.3.

GENUS *DOLICHOGENIDEA* VIERECK 1911

The genus *Dolichogenidea* was erected by Viereck in 1911 and accepted by Mason (1981). It is abundant and ubiquitous genus containing about 1000 species. Viereck (1911) described *Dolichogenidea* as subgenus of *Apanteles* because of it's elongated genae under which he included *Apanteles (Dolichogenidea) banksi* Viereck under this genus. It resembles with Nixon's *laevigata* group of *Apanteles* except the long cheeks. However, Nixon placed *D. banski* in his *crassicornis* group without observing any specimens. Recently, Mason (1981) supported *Dolichogenidea* as ubiquitous genus of tribe Apantelenii. He placed ulter group of *Apanteles* of Nixon (1967) under this genus. He also added some new combinations under this genus.

He placed the following Nearctic species under the genus *Dolichogenidea* : *A. phthorimiae* Muesebeck, *A. acrobasidis* Mues., *A. tischeriae* Mues., palearctic *A. coleophorae* Wilkinson, *A. lacteicolor* Viereck, *M. ultor* Reinhard *(laevigata* group) Nearctic *A. absonus* Mues., *A. (D) banksi* Vier., *A. betheli* Vier., *A. bushnelli* Mues., *A. cacoeciae* Riley, *A. californicus* Mues., *M clavatus* Provancher, *A. dolicocephalus* Mues., *A. homeosomae* Mues., *A. laspeyresiae* Vier., *A. melanopur* Vier., *A. mintonomi* Vier., *A. oidematophori* Mues., *A. paralechiae* Mues., *A. pertrophon* Mues., *A. renaulti* Mason., *A. thujae* Mues., palearctic *M. annularis* Holifsy, *M. dilectus* Hal., *M. emarginatus* Mees., *A. gracilariae* Wilkinson, *A. holidaii* Marshall, *A. imperator* Wilkin., *M. infimus* Hal., *M. laevigatus* Ratzeburg, *A. lemaries* Nixon, *M. lineipes* Wesmael, *M. longicauda* Wesm., *A. muesoxanthus* Ruschka, *A. phaloniae* Wilkin., *A. praetor* Marshal, *A. princeps* Wilkin., *A. sicarius* Marshal, *A. sodalis* Marshal, *A. sophiae* Papp., *A. sezelenyii* Papp, and *A. victor* Wilkin.

Dolichogenidea is distinguished from *Apanteles* by

1. Punctures of mesonotum typically distinctly separated and never breaking into acicculations posterolaterally,

2. Margin of vanal lobe convex and evenly thickly hairy,

3. First tergite parallel sided or slightly wider apically,

4. Apicolateral areas of propodeum (if distinct) wider than high in the *laevigata* group, however, both the propodeal areolation and mesonotal puncturation are reduced to the point at which they are indistinguishable from the

same characters of the *metacarpalis* group of *Apanteles*. So the separation must be made by the shape of venal lobe and first tergite.

Host larvae typically solitary and attacking Microlepidoptera but, occasionally gregarious and attacking Macrolepidoptera, or both.

Type : *Apanteles (D) banksi* Viereck 1911.

Phylogeny of *Apanteles* and *Dolichogenidea*

Nixon (1965) included *ultor* group of *Apanteles* under *Dolichogenidea* which later Mason (1981) accepted to include under the same genus. However, Mason confirmed *ater* group of *Apanteles* of Nixon under *Apanteles* only. Thus, above group typically possess fully carinated propodeum a feature that Mason hold plasiomorphic in Microgastrinae. However, these groups separated by the following characters (Table 1).

Table 1

		Apanteles (*ater* group)	*Dolichogenidea* (*ultor* group)
1.	Posterolateral area of propodeum.	About as wide as tall.	Wider than tall
2.	Punctures on scutum	Often confluent, usually acicculate posteriorly.	Well separated, never acicculated posteriorly.
3.	Margin of vanal lobe; shape, hairs	Concave to straight, Hairless or some times sparsely hairy.	Convex, rarely flattened; uniformly hairy.
4.	Shape of tergite I	Parallel sided to strongly tapered apically.	Slightly broader apically to parallel sided.

DOLICHOGENIDEA EXIGUVI SP. NOV.

Female (Fig. 21)

2.62 mm in length excluding ovipositor, fore wing 2.5 mm, hind wing 2.02 mm, hind leg 2.82 mm, ovipositor 0.12 mm long; head thorax abdomen black.

Head

Head 0.70 mm, long 0.50 mm broad, black, roughly circular in dorsal view, not punctate, except face; frons depressed due to antennal socket; face hairy; ocelli in triangle, dark brown, shiny, with tubercles; interocellar space 0.17 mm; frontocellar space 0.075 mm; eyes large, black, convex, pubescent; interorbital space 0.32 mm long; labrum dark brown, convex, rectangular plate, sparsely hairy.

Antenna (Fig. 110, 111)

Flagellum without bands, 2.77 mm long, longer than body, blackish brown, densely hairy, placodes arranged in three to four longitudinal rows; scape 0.14 mm long; last antennal segment (Fig. 111) elongately conical, 0.4 mm long; terminal four segments more or less equal in length but reduced in width as compared to *D. mythimna*, second terminal segment slightly shorter than others.

Flagellar Formula

2L/W=3.0, 8L/W=2.6, 14L/W=2.3, L2/14=1.8, W2/14=1.5.

Thorax

Thorax 1.10 mm long, black, broad at base narrow at apex, hairy, pronotum sparsely hairy, scutellum densely hairy, hair long, rugose; mesoscutum punctate, black; tegulae not depressed distance between tegulae 0.90 mm, height of thorax at tegulae 0.54 mm; Propodeum (Fig. 113) rectangular, broader than long, 0.27 mm long, 0.77 mm broad, areolet, basolateral areolation much more nipple shaped; propodeum with costulae, smoothe , except for areola and costulae, mediun carinae absent, laterobasal longitudinal carinae present basolongitudinal carinae prominently 'Y' shaped, spiracles elliptical.

Fore Wing (Fig. 112)

2.5 mm long, transparent, straight, hairy, costa thick, 1.25 mm long; stigma pigmented, pale black, 0.57 mm long, 0.20 mm broad; metacarpus 0.70 mm, radial longer than stigma; radial, medial, parallel, not clearly visible, 0.87 mm, 1.7 mm, 1.0 mm long respectively; mediocubitus 0.95 mm long, first anal 1.05 mm, nervulus 0.12 mm, lateral 0.37 mm long, cubital 0.15 mm, recurrent 0.15 mm, second radiomedial 0.15 mm long, entire wing hairy except anal lobe.

Angle between basal & discoideus 81°, discoideus & recurrent 134°, recurrent & radiomedial 90°, basal & radiomedial 90°, radius & cubitus 48°, and nervellus & discoideus 60°.

Hind Wing (Fig. 115)

Hind wing 2.02 mm long, straight, transparent, hairy, metacarpella 0.87 mm, remaining veins reduced, subcostella 1.8 mm; intercubitella 0.17 mm, nervellus 0.14 mm; vanal lobe comparatively large, convex, hairy.

Hind Leg

2.82 mm long, coxa reddish black, trochanter, femur, tibia yellowish; tarsal segment dark brown; coxa strong, stout, roughly triangular, sparsely punctate, reddish brown, 0.42 mm long; trochanter weak, curved, 0.20 mm long; femur straight, stout, 0.60 mm long, yellowish brown; tibia long, slender, hairy, 0.80 mm long, narrow at base, expanded apically; tibial spurs (Fig 116) more or less equal, outer 0.15 mm long, inner 0.13 mm long hairy; basitarsus 0.35 mm long; tarsal segment second, third, fourth and fifth 0.12 mm, 0.09, 0.07 mm, and 0.10 mm respectively; claw 0.075 mm long.

Abdomen

Abdomen, 0.84 mm long, roughly spindle shaped, sparsely hairy, reddish black, posterior margin of each segment black coloured; first tergite (Fig. 114) longer than broad, barrel shaped, bulgging at ¼ basal area and also at middel area, 0.30 mm broad, 0.62 mm long, rugose; second tergite black coloured, broader than long, 0.15 mm long, 0.32 mm broad, basally rugose, acicculated; third tergite 0.31 mm long, 0.36 mm broad; second and third tergite more or less equal in length, testaceous, tip of abdomen with tuft of long hairs on ventral side; ovipositor (Fig. 117) pointed, curved, 0.12 mm long, smooth; ovipositor sheath and ovipositor more or less equal in length, ovipositor sheath 0.10 mm long; hypopygium short, transparent, acutely pointed, 0.9 mm long.

Colour

Reddish black - coxa,

Pale black - stigma,

Blackish brown - antenna,

Black - head, thorax, abdomen.

Male

Male smaller than female, 2.13 mm long, structurally similar to female except sexual characters.

Cocoon

Yellowish white, 2.51 mm long, 1.69 mm broad, gregarious, colony contain 23 cocoons.

Host

The lucerne caterpillar, *Spodoptera exiguva* (Hbn.) (Fig. 35)

The tobacco caterpillar, *Spodoptera litura* (Fab.) (Fig. 33).

Host Plant

The pea, *Pisum sativum* (L.).

Holotype

Female, India, Maharashtra, Coll. 6.VIII.94 Shahuwadi (Kolhapur), (M.S.), Bhoje P.M., antenna, wings, leg, propodeum, tergites, ovipositor on slide labelled as above.

Paratype

Male 45, female 48, sex ratio (M:F) 1:1.2, Coll. from Oct. to Feb. same data as above.

PLATE - XXI

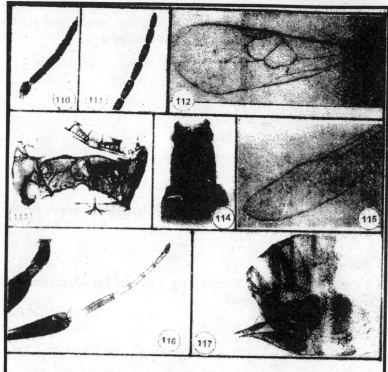

DOLICOGENIDEA EXIGUVI SP. NOV.

Fig. 110 : Antennal basal segments

Fig. 111 : Antennal terminal segments

Fig. 112 : Fore wing

Fig. 113 : Propodeum

Fig. 114 : Tergites

Fig. 115 : Hind Wing

Fig. 116 : Leg

Fig. 117 : Ovipositor

Distributional Record

Maharashtra : ♂16, ♀18, Shahagad (Jalana), 6.VII.94; ♂14, ♀15, Murud (Latur), 19.X.97; ♂15, ♀15, Waduj (Satara), 17.X.93.

DISCUSSION

In Wilkinson's key this species runs close to *Apanteles hemithae* (Mues.) by having second tergite rugose and ovipositor sheath smaller than basitarsus, it also runs close to *Apanteles ricinii* (Bhatnagar) by having propodeum smooth except for areola and costulae (Rao 1961). While, in Nixon's key (1967) the above species runs close to *Apanteles lipsis* (Viereck) by having hind tibia yellow and propodeum smooth. However, it differs from above species by following characters:

(1)   Antennal terminal four segments are more or less equal in length but reduced in width,

(2)   Propodeum with basal lateral areolation much more nipple shaped and with very prominent basolongitudinal 'Y' shaped carinae,

(3)   Tergite first bulgging at ¼ of basal area and also at the middle area,

(4)   Ovipositor sheath and ovipositor more or less equal,

(5)   Tip of abdomen with tuft of long hairs at ventral side,

(6)   Angle between radius and cubitus 48°,

(7)   Flagellar formula :
        2L/W=3.0, 8L/W=2.6, 14L/W=2.3, L2/14=1.8, W2/14=1.5.

DOLICHOGENIDEA LYCOPERCI SP. NOV.

Female (Fig. 22)

2.82 mm long excluding ovipositor, reddish brown, fore wing 2.30 mm long, hind wing 1.7 mm long, hind leg 2.95 mm, ovipositor 0.12 mm long, head reddish brown, thorax dark brown, abdomen yellowish brown.

Head

Head roughly elliptical in dorsal view, 0.62 mm long, 0.60 mm broad, blackish brown, not punctate, smooth, cheek acicculated, sparsely hairy; frons depressed at antennal base; ocelli arranged in triangle, dark red; interorbital space 0.12 mm; frontocellar space 0.075 mm; interocellar space 0.15 mm; eyes dark red, pubescent, convex, large.

Antenna (Fig. 118)

Antenna filiform, 18 segmented, flagellum yellowish brown, hairy, 3.00 mm long, longer than body; length of scape and pedicel 0.12 mm, and 0.02 mm respectively, last antennal segment (Fig. 118) pointedly conical and typical rounded at base, palcodes arranged in two to three longitudinal rows.

Flagellar formula

2L/W=4.0, 8L/W=3.5, 14L/W=2.5, L2/14=1.6, W2/14=1.0.

Thorax

Thorax 0.95 mm long, dark brown with red tinge, densely hairy, punctate, broad at base, narrow at apex; pronotum convex, shield like, hairy, reddish brown, with deepenings, rugose; scutellum blackish brown; height of thorax at tegula 0.40 mm; distance between tegulae 0.60 mm; tegula yellowish brown; metanotum rugulose, hairy, long haired; Propodeum (Fig. 120) squarish, sparsely hairy, reddish brown, broader than long, 0.25 mm long, 0.70 mm broad, areolet, areola open at anterior and with transverse strong carinae on either side, areola strongly marked, basal carinae present, laterolongtudinal carinae present.

Fore Wing (Fig. 119)

2.30 mm long, straight, transparent, hairy except anal margin; costa 1.07 mm long; stigma dark brown, 0.50 mm long, 0.15 mm broad; metacarpus 0.65 mm; radial medial, subdiscoideus poorly visible 0.87 mm, 0.97 mm, 0.82 mm long respectively; mediocubital 0.82 mm, first anal 0.97 mm, lateral 0.25 mm, cubitus 0.15 mm, nervulus 0.10 mm, recurrent vien 0.15 mm, second anal 0.10 mm long.

Angle between basal & discoideus 115°, discoideus & recurrent 144°, recurrent & radiomedial 94°, basal & radiomedial 70°, radius & cubitus 60° and nervulus & discoideus 70°.

Hind Wing

Hing wing 1.70 mm long, straight, transparent, hairy, except subcostal margin; subcostella 1.07 mm long, metacarpella 0.35 mm, intercubitella 0.12 mm; radialla, medialla, cubitella poorly visible and 0.87 mm, 0.80 mm, 0.80 mm respectively; vanal lobe small, uniformly convex and hairy; nervellus 0.21 mm long.

Hind Leg

2.95 mm long, longer than body, reddish brown; coxa red, punctate, punctures more at base, triangular, 0.40 mm; trochanter feeble, slightly curved, 0.20 mm long; femur stout, strong, straight, reddish brown, 0.62 mm long; tibia straight reddish brown, stout, smooth, 0.75 mm long; tibial spurs (Fig. 121) unequal, inner 0.14 mm long outer 0.10 mm long; basitarsus straight, 0.40 mm long; tarsal segment second, third, fourth and fifth 0.17 mm, 0.12 mm, 0.10 mm and 0.12 mm long respectively; claw 0.075 mm long.

Abdomen

Abdomen 1.25 mm long excluding ovipositor, sparsely hairy, yellowish brown in colour except first two tergite and last few abdominal segments blackish yellow; first tergite (Fig. 122) longer than broad, parallel sided, having noticeable median longitudinal carinae, considerably bulgging at ¼ length at base, 0.25 mm broad, 0.40 mm long, rugose, sparsely hairy; second tergite strongly rugulose, broader than long, 0.40 mm broad, 0.19 mm long; basal field of tergite second and third very much wider than apical

PLATE - XXII

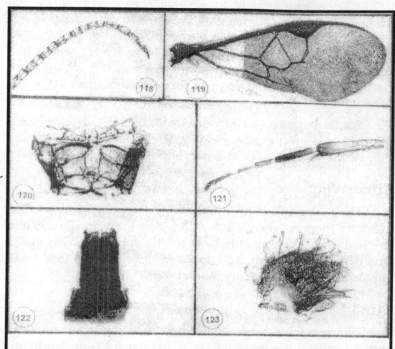

DOLICOGENIDEA LYCOPERCI SP. NOV.

Fig. 118 : Antennal terminal segments
Fig. 119 : Fore wing
Fig. 120 : Propodeum
Fig. 121 : Leg
Fig. 122 : Tergites
Fig. 123 : Ovipositor

width of first tergite; third tergite smooth, yellow, 0.40 mm broad, 0.40 mm long; ovipositor (Fig. 123) pointed, 0.12 mm long, curved, longer than sheath; ovipositor sheath rod like, hairy, tuft of hairs at the tip of sheath, sheath not longer than basal joint of hind tarsus; hypopygium semitransparent, pointed.

Colour

Yellowish brown - abdomen, antenna,

Reddish brown - leg,

Dark brown - thorax, stigma,

Blackish brown - head.

Male

2.37 mm long, smaller than female, structurally similar to female except sexual character.

Cocoon

Cottony white, 3.00 mm long, 1.2 mm broad, gregarious, colony contain about 40 cocoons.

Host

Unidentified lepidopterous larva on tomato.

Host Plant

The tomato, *Lycopersicum vesculantum* (L.).

Holotype

Female, India, Maharashtra, Dahiwadi, on Tomato, Coll. Bhoje P.M., date 22.XII.94.

Paratype

Male 74 female 106, sex ratio (M:F), 1:1.4, Coll, from Aug to Sept., same data as above.

Distributional Record

Maharashtra : ♂15, ♀26, Dahiwadi (Satara), 7.IX.97; ♂13, ♀19, Kasegon (Sangli), 29.III.92; ♂16, ♀20 Waduj (Satara), 17.X.93; ♂13, ♀15, Karad (Satara), 7.XI.93; ♂17, ♀26, Warnanagar (Kolhapur) 6.XII.93.

DISCUSSION

This species runs close to *Apanteles longitangiae* R. and K. in Rao's key (1961) by having second tergite shorter than third and tegulae red testaceous. It also runs close to *Apanteles hemitheae* Wilkinson by having first tergite with noticeable median longitudinal carina and sheath of ovipositor not longer than basal joint of hind tarsus. It also runs close to the same species in Nixon's key (1967) by having ovipositor sheath smaller than hind tibia. However, it differs from above species by having following characters,

(1) Head not punctate,

(2) Pronotum shows deepenings,

(3) Tergite first considerably bulgging at ¼ length at base,

(4) Propodeum with an areola open at anterior and with transverse strong carinae on either sides,

(5) Ovipositor sheath with bunch of hairs at the tip,

(6) Ovipositor curved,

(7) Length of third tergite as equal as length of first tergite,

(8) Tergite third smooth,

(9) Vanal lobe uniformly convex and hairy,

(10) Angle between radius and cubitus 60°,

(11) Flagellar formula:
2L/W=4.0, 8L/W=3.5, 14L/W=2.5, L2/14=1.6, W2/14=1.0.

DOLICHOGENIDEA MYTHIMNA SP. NOV.

Female (Fig. 23)

2.61 mm long, including ovipositor, fore wing 2.20 mm long, hind wind 1.82 mm long, hind leg 2.65 mm, ovipositor 0.12 mm; head dark brown, thorax anteriorly dark brown, posteriorly testaceous, ovipositor sheath dark brown, tip black; abdomen citrunus.

Head

Head oval in dorsal view, 0.69 mm long, 0.52 mm broad, brownish yellow, punctate, hairy, dorsal region sparsely hairy, ventrolaterally densely hairy, hair long; vertex sparsely punctate to smooth; frons and face in comparison with vertex more punctate; frons depressed at antennal base, cetaceous; ocelli in triangle, dark brown, shiny; interocellar space 0.15 mm long; frontocellar space 0.075 mm long; eyes large, brownish, pubescent; labrum rectangular, suspended, convex plate, hairy, punctate; interorbital space 0.37 mm.

Antenna (Fig. 124, 125)

Filliform, brown coloured with transverse thin white band, 18 segmented; scape 0.15 mm long; flagellum 2.75 mm long, longer than body; placodes arranged in three longitudinal rows; terminal four segments more or less equal in length except last, last terminal segment (Fig. 125) spinely pointed, conical, second terminal more or less quadrangular, third & fourth narrower basally.

Flagellar formula

2L/3=3.0, 8L/W=2.3, 14L/W=2.0, L2/14=1.5, W2/14=1.0

Thorax

Thorax 0.92 mm long, yellowish brown to black, punctate; tegulae not depressed, dark brown; scutellum, metanotum strongly rugosely punctate; distance between tegulae 0.60 mm, height of throax at tegulae 0.45 mm; mesoscutum tuberculated, densely hairy; mesosternum cetaceous, shield like; Propodeum (Fig. 127) rectangular, broader than long, hairy, 0.20 mm long, 0.55 mm broad; propodeum and costulae with aerola; propodeum with basal lateral areolation some what nipple shaped and giving two branches from its tip, without median longitudinal carinae; spiracles elliptical.

Fore Wing (Fig. 126)

2.20 mm long, transparent, straight, hairy; stigma pale brown, 0.50 mm long, 0.15 mm broad; costa 1.05 mm long; first anal 0.95 mm long; lateral 0.25 mm; first recurrent vein equal to stigma, 0.50 mm; recurrent 0.15 mm, nervulus 0.10 mm long, cubital 0.15; medio cubitus 0.83 mm long; metacarpus 0.62 mm long; radial, medial, parallel, indistinct, 0.85 mm, 0.77 mm, 0.72 mm long, respectively, r-1 equal to breadth of the stigma, second radiomedial 0.10 mm, entire wing hairy except anal lobe.

Angle between basal & discoideus 100°, discoideus & recurrent 144°, recurrent & radiomedial 100°, basal & radiomedial 70°, radius & cubitus 90° and nervulus & discoideus 85°.

Hind Wing (Fig. 129)

Hind wing 1.82 mm long, transparent, smaller than fore wing, entire wing hairy, vanal lobe small, convex; subcostella 0.8 mm, intercubitella indistinct, 0.10 mm; radialla, medialla, indistinct; nervellus 0.15 mm, intermedialla 0.12 mm, radialla 0.70 mm, cubitella 0.62 mm.

Hind Leg

2.65 mm long, coxa reddish brown; femur broad at base, tapered at apex, blackish brown; tibia yellowish brown; tarsal segments reddish brown at base and dark black at apex; coxa triangular, stout, smooth reddish black, 0.38 mm long; trochanter thin and slender, curved, 0.12 mm long; femur straight, stout, 0.45 mm long, reddish black; tibia long, slender, hairy, 0.69 mm long, narrow at base; tibial spurs (Fig. 128) slightly unequal, outer 0.12 mm and inner 0.10 mm long; basitarsus 0.28 mm long; tarsal segment second third, fourth and fifth 0.19 mm, 0.16 mm, 0.14 mm and 0.18 mm respectively; claws 0.061 mm long.

PLATE - XXIII

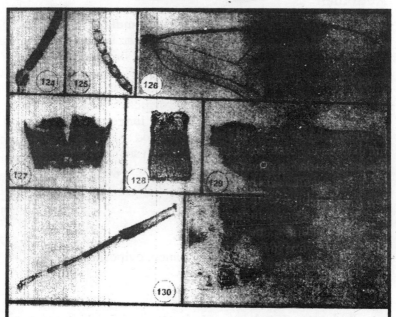

DOLICOGENIDEA MYTHIMNA SP. NOV.

Fig. 124 : Antennal basal segments

Fig. 125 : Antennal terminal segments

Fig. 126 : Fore wing

Fig. 127 : Propodeum

Fig. 128 : Tergites

Fig. 129 : Hind wing

Fig. 130 : Leg

Fig. 131 : Ovipositor

Abdomen

Abdomen 1.26 mm long, some what spindle shaped, blackish dorsally, yellowish ventrally, entire abdomen sparsely punctate, hairy; first tergite (Fig. 128) narrow basally, broad apically, more or less barrel shaped, broader than long, 0.37 mm long, 0.30 mm broad; first and second tergite, rugose, blackish brown, coarsely sculptured, longer than second tergite; ovipositor (Fig. 131) slightly curved, yellowish brown, considerably longer than ovipositor sheath, 0.12 mm long; ovipositor sheath rod shaped, hairy tufts of long hair at tip of sheath, ovipositor sheath shorter than hind tibia, not longer than basitarsus; hypopygium slightly shorter than ovipositor sheath, not actually pointed, dark brown at tip, yellowish brown at middle, hairy.

Colour

Yellowish brown : thorax, abdomen, ovipositor sheath,

Pale brown : stigma,

Dark brown : head, antenna, leg,

Black : coxa, tarsal segments, last three abdominal segments.

Male

2.30 mm long, smaller than female structurally similar except sexual characters.

Cocoon

Yellowish, 2.45 mm long, 1.35 mm in width, gregarious, colony contain 37 cocoons.

Host

The army worm, *Mythimna separata* (Walk.) (Fig. 38).

Host Plant

The jowar, *Sorghum vulgarae* (Pers.).

Holotype

Female, India, Maharashtra. Coll., 10.X.93, Kolhapur (M.S.),

Bhoje P.M., antenna, wings, leg, propodeum, tergites, ovipositor, on slide labelled as above.

Paratype

Male 37, female 78, sex ratio (M : F), 1:2.1 same data as above.

Distributional Record

Maharashtra : ♂8, ♀16, Gaganbawada (Kolhapur), 12.X.95; ♂7, ♀15, Panhala (Kolhapur), 24.XI.93; Shivaji University Campus (Kolhapur), 10.X.93; ♂9, ♀14, Karad (Satara), 13.XII.93; ♂8, ♀18, Kagal (Kolhapur), 25.IX.94.

DISCUSSION

This species runs to *Apanteles valvulae* Rao and Kurian by having length of vein r equal to breadth of stigma and scutellum & metanotum strongly punctate (Rao, 1961). This species also runs close to *Apanteles taenioticornis* (Wilkinson) by having flagellum white banded in Wilkinson's key. In key of Nixon (1967) it resembles with *Apanteles oidematophori* (Mues.) by having following characters, apical segment of front tarsus without trace of spine and ovipositor sheath not longer than basitarsus. However, the present species differs from above species by following characters:

(1)   Vertex partly punctate,

(2)   Tibial spurs slightly unequal,

(3)   Propodeum hairy with basal lateral areolation some what nipple shaped and giving two branches from its tip,

(4)   Ovipositor considerably longer than ovipositor sheath,

(5)   Ovipositor sheath with tuft of hairs at tip,

(6)   Angle between radius and cubitus 90°,

(7)   Flagellar formula :
       $2L/W=3.0$, $8L/W=2.3$, $14L/W=2.0$, $L2/14=1.5$, $W2/14=1.0$.

DOLICHOGENIDEA SUNFLOWARI SP. NOV.

Female (Fig. 19)

3.48 mm long excluding ovipositor, blackish dark brown, fore wing 2.97 mm long, hind wing 2.00 mm, hind leg 3.51 mm long, ovipositor 0.14 mm long; head black, thorax blackish brown, abdomen yellowish brown.

Head

0.75 mm wide, roughly circular in dorsal view, black hairy, 0.60 mm long, punctate; vertex and frons sparsely hairy, hair short, fine; frons depressed at the base of antenna; face roughly rectangular, moderately hairy, hairs long; clypeus some what squarish, plate like; labrum broad rectangular, brown, hairy, convex; ocelli in triangle; interocellar space 0.18 mm long, interorbital space 0.45 mm long; frontocellar space 0.075 mm; eyes large, convex, shining, pubescent, black.

Antenna (Fig. 132, 133)

Filiform 4.05 mm long, 18 segmented including scape and pedicel, yellowish brown, hairy; placodes arranged in four to five longitudinal rows, last antennal segment (Fig. 133) narrowly and elongately cone shaped, scape 0.15 mm long, pedicel 0.03 mm, last three antennal segments considerably reduced in diameter.

Flagellar formula

2L/W=0.2, 8L/W=0.1, 14L/W=0.1, L2/14=1.4, W2/14=1.

Thorax

Thorax 1.35 mm long, blackish brown, densely hairy, mesoscutum punctate, scutellum sparsely punctate; scutum densely punctate, deep punctured; mesosternum large plate like; tegula reddish yellow, depressed due to wing base, distance between tegula 0.80 mm, height of thorax at tegulae 0.92 mm; mesonotum punctate, blackish brown; Propodeum (Fig. 135) rectangular, 0.60 mm broad, 0.30 mm long, broader than long, without areola and without costulae, two longitudinal carinae arise from mediolateral basal portion, lateral carinae joined to longitudinal forming 'T' shaped structure and quadrangular with the posterolateral longitudinal carinae of each side.

Fore Wing (Fig. 134)

2.97 mm long transparent, hairy except at anal margin; costa 2.10 mm long, yellow, thick hairy; stigma hairy black, pigmented, 0.30 mm in length, 0.15 mm broad, smaller than radius; metacarpus 0.42 mm long; radial, medial, parallel, poorly seen; subdiscoideus 0.15 mm long, recurrent 0.15 mm, nervulus 0.9 mm, second radiomedial 0.9 mm long.

Angle between basal & discoideus 95°, discoideus & recurrent 120°, recurrent & radiomedial 80°, basal & radiomedial 65°, radius & cubitus 60° and nervulus & discoideus 70°.

Hind Wing (Fig. 136)

Straight, 2.00 mm long, transparent, hairy membranous subcostella thick basally, hairy, 1.40 mm long; intercubitella 0.10 mm; radialla, medialla and cubitella 0.15 mm, 1.12 mm and 0.85 mm long respectively and poorly visible, anal lobe comparatively larger than brachinal lobe, small nervellus distinct, 0.22 mm long.

Hind Leg

3.52 mm long, shorter than body, brownish black, coxa black, roughly triangular, 0.45 mm long; trochanter curved, brown, 0.18 mm long; femur dark red, testaceous, straight, flattened, 0.85 mm long, tibia, slender, straight, narrow basally, flat apically, 0.90 mm, tibial spurs (Fig. 137) unequal, hairy, brownish yellow, pointed, outer 0.21 mm long, inner 0.15 mm long, half in length of basitarsus; basitarsus slender, straight, 0.50 mm long; tarsal segment second, third, fourth, and fifth 0.18 mm, 0.13 mm, 0.12 mm, and 0.13 mm long respectively; claw short, hairy, 0.07 mm long.

Abdomen

1.53 mm long, excluding ovipositor, ovoid, sparsely hairy, broad at base, pointed at apex, yellowish brown; first tergite (Fig. 138) blackish, with fine hairs, rugulose apically, smooth basally, basally dilated at its ¼ height, 0.45 mm long, 0.30 mm broad; second tergite blackish anteriorly, brownish laterally, longer than broad, 0.35 mm long, 0.25 mm broad, smaller than first tergite; third tergite brownish, yellow middorsally, brownish laterally, longer than broad, 0.35 mm long, 0.30 mm broad; equal in length of second tergite; fourth tergite 0.30 mm long and 0.18 mm broad; ovipositor (Fig. 139), curved not accutely pointed, smooth, 0.14 mm, longer than ovipositor sheath, sheath hairy long hairs bunch at the tip, tip black coloured; small hairs sparsely distributed on sheath, sheath wider than ovipositor; hypopygium membranous and pointed, blackish brown at the tip, last tergite ventrally tufty hairy.

Colour

Yellowish brown - abdomen, antenna,

Brownish black - leg,

Brownish yellow - tibial spurs,

Blackish brown - thorax,

Black - stigma, coxa, head.

Male

2.90 mm long, smaller than female, structurally similar to the female, except sexual characters.

Cocoon

3.20 mm long, 2.5 mm broad, gregarious, cottony white; a colony contain about 60 cocoons.

Host

The bihar hairy caterpillar, *Spilosoma obliqua* (Wlk.) (Fig. 36).

Host Plant

The sunflower, *Helianthus annus* L.

Holotype

Female, India, Maharashtra, Coll. 18.VIII.96, Sambhapur, M.S., Bhoje P.M., antenna, wings, leg, propodeum, tergites, ovipositor on ⁻lide labelled as above.

PLATE - XXIV

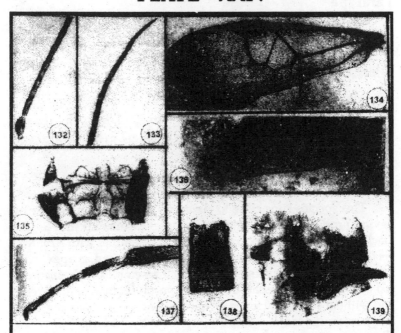

DOLICOGENIDEA SUNFLOWARI SP. NOV.

Fig. 132 : Antennal basal segments

Fig. 133 : Antennal terminal segments

Fig. 134 : Fore wing

Fig. 135 : Propodeum

Fig. 136 : Hind wing

Fig. 137 : Leg

Fig. 138 : Tergites

Fig. 139 : Ovipositor

Paratype

Male 51, female 93, sex ratio (M:F) (1:1.8), Coll. from Aug. to Feb., same data as above.

Distributional Record

Maharashtra : ♂24, ♀60, Sambhapur (Kolhapur), 18.VIII.96; ♂5, ♀13, Palus (Sangali), 25.VIII.93; ♂6, ♀15, Mayani (Satara), 10.XI.96; ♂7, ♀18, Borpadale (Kolhapur), 24.XI.93; ♂27, ♀33, Bidkin (Aurangabad), 31.X.93.

DISCUSSION

This species runs close to *Apanteles pachkuriae* Bhatnagar by having propodeum with transverse basal carina and first tergite blackish (Rao, 1961). In Wilkinson's key, it resembles with *Apanteles hyblaeae* (Wilkinson) by having first tergite as broad as apex, hind femora red-testaceous. In Nixon's key it resembles with *Apanteles fakhralhajiae* Mahdihassan by having propodeum without areola and without costulae. However, the present species *Dolichogenidea sunflowari* differs from above species by having following characters:

(1) Tibial spurs unequal,

(2) Head punctate,

(3) Tergite first rugulose apically, smooth basally, slightly wider apically, basally dilated at its's ¼ height,

(4) In propodeum, two longitudinal carinae arise from mediolateral basal portion, lateral carinae joined to longitudinal forming 'T' shaped structure and quadrangular with the posterolateral longitudinal carinae of each side,

(5) Ovipositor shorter than tibia,

(6) Angle between radius and cubitus 60°,

(7) Flagellar formulla :
2L/W=0.2, 8L/W=0.1, 14L/W=0.1, L2/14=1.4, W2/14=1.

GENUS *GLYPTAPANTLES* ASHMEAD 1905

The genus *Glyptapantales* is one of larger segregates of old *Apanteles* errected by Ashmead (1905). Recently, Manson (1981) reclassified the sub family microgastrinae and placed about 25 per cent of the species from tropics and about 10 per cent from temperate regions of old *Apanteles* under this genus. He palced the groups of old *Apanteles* like *virtipennis, octonarius, pallpies, siderion, demeter, fraternus* and *triangulator* and most of the species of Wilkinson's group 'A' under this genus. The speciality of *vitripennis* is that it is well developed in cool and humid temperate climates while, the *octonarius* is well represented in humid temperate and tropical climates. However, from dry climates, *Glyptapanteles* is rarely represented. Some more important species which Mason (1981) placed under this genus are mentioned below:

Apanteles caffreyi Muesebeck, *A. cussianus* Riley, *A. floridanus* Mues., *Microgaster militaris* Walsh; *A. herbertii* Ashmead, *A. nigricornis* Mues., *A. websteri* Mues., *vitipennis* group *A. politus* Riley, *P. altocole* Ashm., *A. compressus* Mues., *A. compressiventris* Mues., *A. flavourariateles* Mues., *A. pallipes* Reinhard, *A. witeripennis* Mues. and *A. surothripae* Weed.

About 30 per cent species of old *Apanteles* are included form Nearctic region under this genus. In addition, the exotic species, *Microgaster vitripennis* Curtis, *M. flavipes* Haliday, *M. includes* Ratzeburg, *M. liparidis* Bouche, *A. veter* Nixon, *M. triangulator* Wesm., *A. thompsoni* Lyle, *A. fraternus* Mues., *A. parthetriae* Mues., *A. sagmaria* Nixon, *A. concinnus* Mues., *A. africanus* Viereck, *A. malthacae* Mues., *A. benifius* Vier., *A. cucosame* Wilkinson, *A. gowdeyli* Gahan, *A. laxatus* Wilkinson, *A. demeter* Wilkinson have also added to *Glyptapanteles* by Mason (1981). From India, very little attention is given on the genus *Glyptapanteles*. Only two species have been reported under this genus (Sathe & Inamadar, 1991; Dawale, 1991).

Type : (*G. manilae* Ashmead 1905)

=*Apanteles ashmeadi* Wilkinson 1928.

Wilkinson proposed *A. ashmeadi* as a new name for the secondary homonym, *G. manilae* (Ashm.) 1905 (not *A. manilae* Ashm. 1904) when he transferred the former species to *Apanteles*. The replacement name is permanent (Art-Sq (b) (i), amended 1972, *Bul. Zool. Nom. 29* : 180).

GLYPTAPANTELES MELANITISI SP. NOV.

Female (Fig. 26)

3.12 mm long, excluding ovipositor, fore wing 2.95 mm long, hind wing 2.15 mm long, hind leg 3.15 mm long, ovipositor 0.17 mm long, head, thorax, abdomen black.

Head

Head black, elliptical in dorsal view, convex below antenna in lateral view, ventrally rectangular, hairy, pubescent, 0.74 mm long, 0.66 mm broad; vertex frons sparsely hairy, punctate; frons flat, deeply granulated; antennal socket shiny, broad; face roughly rectangular, hairy with long hair; emarginate; clypeus brownish black, not distinctly separate, close to molar space, punctate, plate like; labrum broad, dark brown, semicircular; ocelli in triangle, with small tubercles; intercellar space 0.18 mm; frontocellar space 0.071 mm; eyes large, convex, pubescent elliptical, shiny, black; interorbital space 0.36 mm long.

Antenna (Fig. 140, 141)

Antenna deep brown, 3.75 mm long, longer than body, 16 segmented excluding scape pedicel hairy; scape 0.16 mm; placodes two to four in longitudinal rows, last antennal segment elongated, cone shaped, terminal first segment (Fig. 141) 0.12 mm, second 0.09 mm, third 0.08 mm long, terminal segment longer than penultimate and fourth terminal segment approximately twice the length of segment second and third.

Flagellar Formula

2L/W=1.9, 8L/W=1.7, 14L/W=0.45, L2/14=1, W2/14=1.02.

Thorax

Black, densely hairy, roughly spindle shaped, 1.10 mm long; scutellum large, sculptured, lateral region with shallow punctures, flat, plate like, slightly convex; mesoscutellum small, convex; scutellum and mesoscutellum punctate; mesoscutellum broad, plate like rugose; mesonotum black, punctate; tegulae slightly depressed, black, coarse, distance in between tegulae 0.90

mm; height of thorax at tegulae 0.78 mm; Propodeum (Fig. 143) large, some what semicircular, 0.48 mm long, 0.69 mm broad, without areola, carinae two, originated from mid dorsal at lower base, shiny, branched carinae absent, carinae extended on either side, spiracles elliptical.

Fore Wing (Fig. 142)

2.95 mm long, straight, transparent, hairy, except anal margin; costa thick, hairy, 1.45 mm long; stigma black, smaller than radius, hairy hyaline, smaller than metacarpus, 0.65 mm long, 0.24 mm broad; metacarpus 0.78 mm long; radial, medial and subdiscoidus 1.00 mm, 1.21 mm, 0.97 mm long, respectively; mediocubitus 1.00 mm first anal 0.12 mm long, basal 0.40 mm, recurrent 0.20 mm, nervulus 0.12 mm long, second radiomedial 0.18 mm long.

Angle between basal & discoideus 80°, discoideus & recurrent 125°, recurrent & radiomedial 115°, basal & rediomedial 70°, radious & cubitus 74° and nervulus & discoideus 75°.

Hind Wing (Fig. 144)

2.15 mm long, transparent, straight, hairy except subcostal margin; subcostella 1.40 mm long, intercubitella 0.15 mm long, remaining veins reduced or absent, vanal lobe leaf like, convex, with tuft of hair nervellus 0.30 mm.

Hind Leg

3.15 mm long, longer than body, brownish-yellow; coxa blackish brown, triangular, 0.30 mm in length; trochanter triangular, 0.18 mm in length; femur stout, brown, 0.81 mm long, citrunus, slender, broader at distal end and tapering at base, 0.81 mm in length; tibial spurs (Fig. 145), unequal, pointed, hairy, yellow, outer 0.21 mm long, inner 0.15 mm long; basitarsus 0.45 long; second, third, fourth and fifth segments, 0.18, 0.12, 0.19 and 0.12 mm in length respectively; claw 0.09 mm in length.

Abdomen

1.27 mm in length excluding ovipositor, dark brown, hairy, yellowish bands present; tergites dark brown at apex; first abdominal tergite (Fig. 146) black with fine hair, rugose, broad basally, apically narrow and 'U' shaped notched basally, decorated by carinae, 0.49 mm long, 0.12 mm broad; second tergite (Fig. 146) blackish mid-dorsally, brownish laterally, rugulose, 0.18 mm long, 0.15 mm broad, some what triangular; third tergite, mid-dorsally dark brown, laterally yellowish brown, borader than long 0.25 mm broad, 0.25 mm long; rest tergites narrow posteriorly; ovipositor short (Fig. 147) pointed, hairy, brownish, 0.15 mm long, smaller than hind femora; ovipositor sheath (Fig. 147) slightly longer than ovipositor, 0.18 mm long, considerably shorter than abdomen.

Colour

Yellow - tibial spurs,

Brown - femur,

Deep brown - antenna, abdomen,

Blackish brown - coxa,

Black - head, thorax, stigma.

Male

2.97 mm long, smaller than female, structurally similar to female, except sexual characters.

Cocoon

2.8 mm long, 1.7 mm broad, gregarious, cottony white, each colony contain 30 to 40 cocoons (Fig. 39).

Host

The rice butterfly larva, *Melanitis ismene* Cramer (Fig. 40).

Host Plant

The paddy, *Oryzae sativa* L.

Holotype

Female, India, Maharashtra, Coll. 23.IX.94, Panhala, M.S., Bhoje, P.M., antenna, wings, leg, propdeum, tergites, ovipositor, on slide labelled as above.

PLATE - XXV

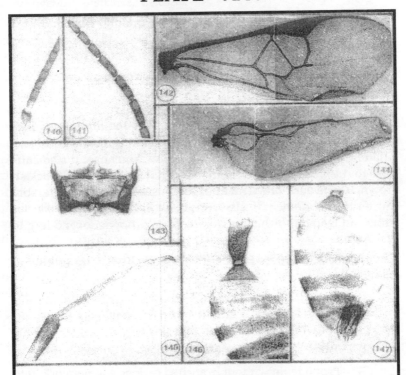

GLYPTAPANTELES MALANTIS SP. NOV.

Fig. 140 : Antennal basal segments
Fig. 141 : Antennal terminal segments
Fig. 142 : Fore wing
Fig. 143 : Propodeum
Fig. 144 : Hind wing
Fig. 145 : Leg
Fig. 146 : Tergites
Fig. 147 : Ovipositor

Paratype

Male 10, female 20, sex ratio (M:F), 1:2, same data as above.

Distributional Record

Maharashtra : ♂10, ♀20 Gaganbawada (Kolhapur), 26.XI.95.

DISCUSSION

This species runs close to *Apanteles (=Cotesia) sesamae* Cameron in Rao's key by having mesonotum punctate and head in lateral view conspicusely convex below antennae. It also runs close to *Apanteles obliguae* Wilkinson by having hind coxa blackish brown, tergite dark-brown at apex, ovipositor sheath considerably shorter than abdomen. It also runs close to *Glyptapanteles malshri* Sathe and Inamdar by having no areola on propodeum and tergite first rugose.

However, it differs from above species by having following characters:

(1) Antennal terminal segment longer than penultimate and fourth terminal segment approximately twice the length of the segments second and third,

(2) Tibial spurs unequal,

(3) Propodeum without branched carinae and network, two carinae orginated from mid-dorsal,

(4) Tergite first rugose, broad basally, narrowed apically,

(5) Second tergite rugulose, triangular, blackish mid-dorsally, brownish laterally,

(6) Vanal lobe with tuft of hairs,

(7) Angle between radious and cubitus 74°,

(8) Flagellar formula :
2L/W=1.9, 8L/W=1.7, 14L/W=0.45, L2/14=1, W2/14=0.2.

GENUS : *HYPOMICROGASTER* ASHMEAD 1898

The genus *Hypomicrogaster* is errected by Ashmead in 1898 and supported by Mason (1981). Mason says that is large genus in the new tropical region, where nearly all the species are undescribed, but, four species, only two of which have names, are found in Western, North America. The species Mason (1981) assigned are *Hypomicrogaster acarmis* Nixon, *H. acontes* Nixon, *Microgaster ecdytolophae* Muesebeck, *H. ecus* Nixon, *Eurogaster ecdytolophae* Muesebeck, *H. moscus* Nix., *H. solox* Nix., *H. tydeus* Nix., *M. zonaria* Say, *M. diaphaniae* Mues., *M. jacarae* Mues. The last two species are new combinations. As per Mason (1981) *Hypomicrogaster* is one of the most strongly characterised Microgastrinae genera and should not be confused with any thing else except, *Dolichogenidea* if the very small areolet and concave venal lobe are overlooked. He does not believe that it is directly ancestral to any other genus, in fact, he confirmed as isolated genus.

From USSR two species namely. *H. tiro* Reinh., *H. suffolciensis* Morley have been described (Tobias 1975; Telenga, 1955). From India only one species of this genus have been described (Sathe & Inamadar, 1989).

Type : *Microgaster zonaria* Say.

HYPOMICROGASTER MINERI SP. NOV.

Female (Fig. 27)

3.55 mm long excluding ovipositor, fore wing 2.82 mm long, hind wing 2.30 mm long, hind leg 2.79 mm long, ovipositor 0.10 mm long, black, head, thorax black.

Head

Head black, ellipitical in dorsal view, densely hairy, hair fine, short moderately long, 0.75 mm long and 0.67 mm broad, occipital region with polished glabrous, concave area occupying about half the width of head; occipute hairy on either side, sparsely hairy;vertex and frons sparsely hairy, granular; face roughly rectangular, moderately hairy, hairs long as compared to the hairs of clypeus; tegulae depressed due to antennal socket; labrum, semicircular, convex, dark brown, hairy; ocelli large lying in low; rounded, small, shiny, with tubercles; interocellar space 0.15 mm, frontocellar space 0.050 mm; ocellocular space 0.15 mm; eyes large, elliptical, convex, pubescent, shiny; interorbital space 0.37 mm long.

Antenna (Fig. 148, 149)

Antenna black, 18 segmented including basal scape and pedicel; scape 0.14 mm long; placodes arranged in five to six longitudinal rows, last antennal segment (Fig. 149) small and conical, 0.7 mm in length, last four terminal antennal segments: first, second, third and fourth 0.07 mm, 0.05 mm, 0.06 mm and 0.07 mm long respectively.

Flagellar formula

2L/W=3, 8L/W=2.2, 14L/W=3, L2/14=0.9, W2/14=1.

Thorax

Thorax 1.25 mm long, black, densely hairy, hair moderately long; thorax roughly ovoid, narrow posteriorly, broad anteriorly; pronotum large, semicircular, sides with upper and lower grooves; mesonotum smooth, tegulae depressed, distance between tegulae 0.99 mm long, height of thorax at tegulae 0.45 mm; scutellum large, smooth, with apical band, convex, plate like, various carinae and sutures distinct, sculpture coarse; Propodeum (Fig. 151) rugulose, 0.30 mm long and 0.85 mm broad, with more or less areolation, faint latero-anteriorly, median logitudinal carinae and pair of mediobasal carinae running and forming aerolation, prominent posteriolateral carina runs anteriomedially forming nipple like carination on each side, areola and median carina make unusual combination, spiracles elliptical.

Fore Wing (Fig. 150)

Fore wing 2.82 mm long, straight, transparent, hairy, except at anal margin, narrow basally, broad apically; costa thick, hairy, grey, 1.42 mm long; stigma black, hairy, 0.62 mm long, 0.22 mm broad; metacarpus 0.70 mm long; radius, medial and subdiscoideus poorly distinct, 0.97 mm, 1.20 mm and 0.92 mm long respectively; mediocubitus 1.02 mm long; first anal 1.27 mm long; basal 0.40 mm; cubitus 0.17 mm; nervulus 0.12 mm; recurrent 0.17 mm; second radiomedial 0.17 mm long.

Angle between basal & discoideus 109°, discoideus & recurrent 124°, recurrent & radiomedial 112°, basal & radiomedial 110°, radious & cubitus 75° and nervulus & discoideus 70°.

Hind wing (Fig. 152)

1.45 mm long, transparent; first cubitellan cell longer than wide; radialla 0.17 mm; medialla 0.85 mm long, cubitella 0.95 mm long; vanal lobe small, leaf like, convex, sparsely hairy apically, densely hairy at base; subcostella 1.39 mm long; intercubitella 0.12 mm long; nervellus 0.25 mm long.

Hind Leg

2.79 mm in length; coxa reddish brown, roughly triangular smooth, stout hairy, 0.65 mm long; trochanter slightly curved, yellow, short, 0.30 mm long; femur stout, yellowish brown, 0.75 mm long; tibial spurs unequal, hairy, outer 0.25 mm long, inner 0.22 mm long; basitarsus slender, hairy, 0.47 mm long, tarsal segment second, third, fourth and fifth 0.20 mm, 0.17 mm, 0.12 mm and 0.12 mm long respectively; claw 0.01 mm long; tibial and tarsal segments more hairy than other segments.

PLATE - XXVI

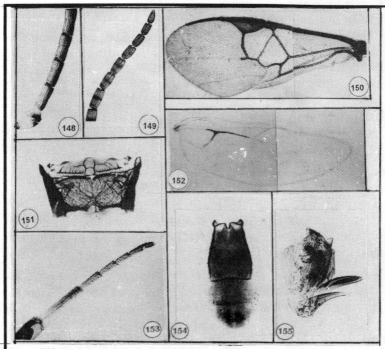

HYPOMICROGASTER MINARI SP. NOV.

Fig. 148 : Antennal basal segments

Fig. 149 : Antennal terminal segments

Fig. 150 : Fore wing

Fig. 151 : Propodeum

Fig. 152 : Hind wing

Fig. 153 : Leg

Fig. 154 : Tergites

Fig. 155 : Ovipositor

Abdomen

Abdomen 1.35 mm long excluding ovipositor, smooth, narrow basally, broad posteriorly, black strips on dorsal side, yellow strips on ventral side, reddish brown laterally; ovipositor blackish-yellow; abdominal tergites (Fig. 154) mid dorsal black, first tergite rugose apically, longer than broad, 0.42 mm broad, 0.37 mm long, broadened middle, with U shaped notch, excavated basally, second tergite rugose, black and punctate, broader than long, 0.20 mm broad, 0.50 mm long, smooth at middle; third tergite more or less equal in length of second tergite, 0.55 mm long, 0.25 mm broad; fourth tergite 0.45 mm long, 0.15 mm broad; remaining tergites narrow posteriorly; ovipositor sheath (Fig. 155) longer than ovipositor, smooth; ovipositor sheath curved, 0.12 mm long, blunt; ovipositor pointed, curved, black, smooth, without hairs, tip faint yellowish brown, 0.10 mm long.

Colour

Yellow : trochanter,

Yellowish brown : femur, ventral strips on abdomen,

Reddish brown : lateral of abdomen, coxa,

Black : head, dorsal of thorax, antenna.

Male

2.67 mm in length, smaller than female, similar to female except sexual characters.

Cocoon

3.00 mm long and 2.00 mm broad, silvery white, gregarious, colony contain about 12 to 16 cocoons.

Host

The jowar stem borer, *Chilo partellus* (Swin.) (Fig. 31).

Host Plant

The Maize, *Zea mays* (Linn.).

Holotype

Female, India, Maharashtra, Coll. 24.XII.94, Phaltan, M.S., Bhoje P.M., antenna, wings, leg, propodeum, tergites, ovipositor on slide labelled as above.

Paratype

Male 49, female 69, sex ratio (M:F), 1:1.4; Coll. from Aug. to Dec., same data as above.

Distributional Record

Maharashtra : ♂22, ♀32, Kalamba (Kolhapur), 4XII94; ♂27, ♀37, Malkapur (Kolhapur), 24.X.96.

DISCUSSION

This species runs close to *Hypomicrogaster zonaria* (Say) by having following characters:

(1)   Propoedeum with areola and median carina forming unsual combination.

(2)   Occipital region of head with polished, glabrous and concave area,

(3)   Second intercubital vein very small (Mason 1981). But, differs from above species by propodeum with nipple like structure on each side and with faint middle carination,

(4)   Ovipositor shorter than sheath,

(5)   First tergite broadended at middle, rugose apically, excavated baselly,

(6)   First tergite with 'U' shaped notch, second tergite smooth at middle and rugose, punctate at basally and apically, third tergite more or less equal to length of second tergite,

(7)   Angle between radious and cubitus 75°,

(8)   Flagellar formula :

2L/W=3, 8L/W=2.2, 14L/W=3, L2/14=0.9, W2/14=1.

CHAPTER 4
BIOLOGICAL CONTROL

Chemical control create several serious problems like air and water pollution, health hazards, killing of beneficial insects, secondary pest out-break, pest-resistance, pest resurgence, etc. Hence, for avoiding pesticidal problems biological control is must and is potential "living weapon" over chemical control.

Definition

Biological control is the action of parasitoids, predators and pathogens against target pests to keep their populations below the level of economic damage by keeping environment hormonized.

Early History

The first biocontrol agent of insect pest is man since he used insects for his diet at eary days, before the start of agriculture. The biological control method was first used by Chinese. They used predatory ants for controlling citrus pests. The first international movement of biological control of pest was reported in 1762 under which Indian mynah bird, *Acridotheres tristis* was imported by Mauritius Govt. to control Red Locust, *Nomadacris septemfasciata*. This bird saved the health of Mauritius people and sugarcane crop at that time. Later, in 1860 the cottony cushion scale insect, *Icerya purchesi* was control by using a predator lady bird beetle, *Rodalia cardinalis* and a parasitoid, *Cryptochaetum icerya*. The pest was introduced unintensionally in california from Australia, since then several insects were controlled by biological means (Debach, 1964).

Ecological basis

Biological control is manipulation of environment against target species. The biocontrol agents are population regulatory factors like temperature, humidity, rainfall, etc. in biological pest

95

control equiiibrium of two populations i.e. pest and biocontrol is maintained by using ecological principles. Hence, the efficacy of biocontrol agent is dependant on ecological factors. Some biocontrol agents colonized within few months but some species required years. Hoever, Clausen (1951) says that if establishment is not evident within 3 years then there is little hope of success of biocontrol programme.

Economics

As compared to chemical control we are spending very less amount on biological control in India. DeBach (1964) reported that during 1923-1953, California industry saved 115 million dollors by spending only 4-5 million dollors on biological control. In general, biological control provides handsome divident to growers. The following table shows economical details.

Table 1 : Economics of biocontrol

Nature enemy (Species)	Dose	Pest species	Required cost (Rs.)
Trichogramma spp.	40,000 / acre	*Chilo* spp.	50-00
Trichogramma spp.	1,00,000 / acre	Erias, Pectinophora, Heliothis	100-00
Bracon brevicornis	1,800 / acre	Black headed caterpillar	120-00
Laptomastix spp.	2,000 / acre	Pests of fruit trees	250-00
Cryptolaemus sp.	600 / acre	Mealy bugs on Coffee / Mulberry	300-00
Scymnus spp.	600 / acre	,,	300-00
Goniozus nephantidis	1200 / acre	Black headed caterpillar	180-00

Applications

The biological control can be applied for the pests of agriculture, forest, medical, veterinary, stored grains and household etc.

Steps

The bioiogical control is tedious job. For the establishment of biological pest control programme, following steps are essential :

1. Taxonomic identification of pest and biocontrol agents.
2. Origin, geographic distribution and ecological requirements of pests and their biocontrol agents.
3. Host parasitoid lists and other faunal survey.
4. Field study of both target and beneficial organisms (biocontrol agents).
5. Prediction of success of efficiency.
6. Collection of beneficial organisms (B.C.A.).
7. Shipment of B.C.A.
8. Quarantine.
9. Propogation.
10. Release and colonization.
11. Follow-up - recoveries and
12. Evaluation.

Methods

In biological pest control, following methods are visualized.

1. Collection and storage or handling the pests to kill (except biocontrol agents).
2. Collection of predators and parasitoids and release in native country.
3. Mass rearing and periodic colonization.
4. Importation of parasitoids / predators / pathogens.

The above methods may be adopted as per the situations and conditions available.

Future of biological control

The chemical control will never solve the permanent problem of pests but, biological control when works, will solve the problem of pests permanently. Secondly, chemical control has several demerits. Hence, biological control has more importance in pest management. The international organizations / agencies like FAO, CIBC, USDA, IOBC, etc. are coming forward to encourage the biological pest suppression by providing knowledge/ideas to researchers, teachers, students, farmers etc. Now a days biological pest control is prestigeous one. Hence, this method of pest control is widely accepted in the world and therefore biological control has bright future.

Biocontrol agents

Parasitoids, predators and pathogens are important biocontrol agents of insect pests. Now a days pathogens are studied under separate head viz. "Microbiol control" and hence not included under biological control.

The parasitoids are entomophagus insects and are different from true parasites. The parasitoids lay their eggs in/on the host body and parasitize them, develop upon the host body and then kill the host at the end of its association. The parasitoids are scattered in several orders of insects like Hymenoptera, Diptera, Lepidoptera, Hemiptera, etc. However, Hymenoptera ranks first as far as the number of species is concerned. According to Kerrich (1960) the existing number of parasitic hymenoptera is about 2,50,000 in the world. The most important families of parasitic hymenoptea are Ichneumonidae, Braconidae, Trichogrammatidae and Chalcideae. 60,000 species of Ichneumonids and 40,000 species of Braconids have been described in the world (Gupta, 1988). Several species of hymenoptera attack the pests of economic importance (Sathe, 1994). *Isotima javensis* attacks sugarcane top borer (*Tryporyza nivella*), *Xanthopimpla punctata* to Jowar stem borer (*Chilo partellus*), *Apanteles* spp to several lepidopterous and homopterous pests. In addition, Encyrtids, Eulophids, Scolids, etc. are also potential biocontrol agents of several insect pests. However, the Trichogrammatids specially, *Trichogramma* spp are very prominantly figured in the biological control programmes of the world. The most significant characteristics of this genus is that they are very small in size and attack very first stage (egg stage) of the pest and check the future damage by pest to crops and thus the population of the target species. The important species of *Trichogramma* used in biological pest suppression are *T. minutum, T. chilonis, T. evanescens, T. australicum, T. brasilensis, T. confusum, T. japonicum, T. armigera, T. orstrinae, and T. acheae*, etc.

From order Diptera the family tachinidae ranks first. More than 1500 parasitic species of tachinidflies are known to science (Askew 1971). They parasitizes several lepidopterous and coleopterous pests of economic importance.

Species of *Trichogramme* are mass reared in China and used against a variety of crop pests of which cotton alone comprised about 6,80,000 ha. annually. In Britain and Netherlands 170 million *Encarsia* spp. and 32 million *Opius* spp. are reared for the control of white flies and olive flies respectively. Several natural enemies have been imported from different countries to control insect pests in India. Some of them are listed in Table-1. In India also, several species of biocontrol agents are mass reared and utilized in biological pest suppression. (Rao *et. al* 1971).

Table 2 : Some biocontrol programmes in India

Sr. No.	Year & Country (Imported)	Natural Enemy	Pest Species	Crop	Established place
1.	1929 Australia	*Radolia cardinalis* (Coleoptera)	*Icerya purchasi* (Hemiptera)	Citrus	T.N., Kerala
2.	1940 USA	*Aphelinus mali* (Hymenoptera)	*Eriosoma lanigerum* (Hemiptera)	Apple	Punjab, Assam, S. India
3.	1960 Zanzibar via Sri Lanka	*Spoggosia beniziana* (Diptera)	*Nephantis serinopa* (Lepidoptera)	Coconut	T.N., Orissa
4.	1964 New Guinea	*Telanomus sp.* (Hymenoptera)	*Achea janata* Lepidoptera	Caster	A.P.
5.	1965 S.U.S.A.	*Trichogramma brasilensis* (Hym.)	*Pectinophora gossypiella* (Lepidoptera)	Cotton	Haryana
6.	1968 S.U.S.A. (California)	*T. brasilensis* (Hymenoptera)	*Heliothis armigera* (Lepidoptera)	*Polyphagus*	Karnataka
7.	1973 Mauritus via East Africa	*Sticholotis medayassa* (Coleptera)	*Melanospis glomerata* (Hamiptera)	sugar-cane	India

DeBatch (1964) reported 120 pest species that have been controlled very successfully in 60 countries by biological means. Rao et. al., (1969) reviewed the bicontrol programmes of South East Asia and recently Chako reviewed the biocontrol of insect pests in India.

In USA there are 50 commercial insectaries which are actively engaged in mass rearing of various parasitoids and predator species. 3,000 million *Trichogramma* sp., 203 million *Aphytis melinus* Debatch, 26 million *Cryptolaemus montrouizeiri* Mulsant and 18 million *Crysoperla carnea* Stephens are mass reared for the control of various lepidopterous pests, scales, mealy bugs and other soft bodied sucking insects.

In USSR more than 10 biological factories are known for producing about 50,000 million *Trichogram* spp. per season. Beside, about 15 species of parasitoids and predators are produced and released in about 10 million hectares for control of variety of pests.

In India, some major pests like sugarcane borers, pyrilla, cotton bollworms, rice stem borer, coconut black headed caterpillar, sugarcane scales and several species of mealy bugs have been controlled by biological means (by using insects). The mass rearing techniques have been developed for many natural enemies of insect pests in India. The notable examples are *Trichogramme* spp. *Chrysopa* sp. Lady bird beetles, etc. There are several potential natural enemies which are not fully exploited in pest control in India. The commercial production of biocontrol agents was started in 1981 in India and now a days, several laboratories are actively engaged in producing biocontrol agents on large scale. The natural enemies presently commercially available include various species of *Trichogramma* for controlling sugarcane borers, cotton boll works, codling moth, *Heliothis armigera* etc. and *Chilonus blackburni*, *Cryptolaemus montrouzleri*, *Crysopa* sp. etc. for several other pests (Table 2).

Application dose : The recommended doses of natural enemies against the pest species are shown in Table 2.

Table 3 : Biocontrol agents available in India and recommended dose

Sr. No.	Species Natural enemy	Pest	Dose recommended
1.	Trichogramma sp.	H. armigera	120,000 / acre
2.	Trichogramma sp.	Chilo sacchariphaga indicus	2,00,000 / ha
3.	Chilonus blackburni	Cotton bollworms	10,000 / week /acre
4.	Bracon krikpatrikii	,,	5,000 / week / acre
5.	Meteorus dichomeridis	Spilosoma obliqua	1,00,000/ha/week
6.	Cryptolaemus montrouzieri	Maconellicoccus hirsutus	@ 250 / adults / ha
7.	Nesolynx thymus	Exorista bombycis	1,000,000 adults females and 500 males in 3 split releases

Disadvantages of biological control

1. Take long time to control pests.
2. It is not suitable for the annual crops.
3. It has slow pace.
4. It is not applicable to all species of the pests.

Advantages

1. It is pollution free and hazard free.
2. It solves the permanent problem of pests when works.
3. It is economic method.

CHAPTER 5

ASPECTS OF BIOLOGICAL CONTROL

In biological control living organisms are used for the suppression of pest populations. Biological control is, "the action of biocontrol agents against the target species to suppress the population below the level of economic damage by keeping environment hormonized". In general, parasitoids, predators and pathogens are used as biocontrol against as they frequently determine population densities of target species by causing mortalities in them.

Parasitoids

Parasitoids are entomophagus, they lay their eggs in/on the host body, parasitize them, develop on the host and then kill at the end of its association. Taxonomical relationship of this group have been studied by several workers. The parasitoids are scattered in several orders like Hymenoptera, Diptera, Lepidoptera, Himiptera etc. But Hymenoptera ranks first. According to Kerrich (1960) the existing number of parasitic hymenoptera might-reach 2,50,000 in the world. The most important families of hymenoptera are Ichneumonideae, Braconidae, Trichogrammatides, and Chalcidae. 60,000 species of Ichneumonids and 40,000 species of Braconids have been described. The taxonomical relationship of parasitoids have been studied by Wilkinson (1928), Bhatnagar (1948) Nixon (1965, 1967) Townes et al., (1961), Rao (1967) Gupta (1987, 1988) Nikam (1982) and Sathe (1993), etc. *Trichogramma* spp. are very prominently figured in the biocontrol programmes in India and abroad. The most significant character of these wasps is that they attack very first stage (i.e. egg stage) of the pest and check the future damage to crop, and population of target species. The important species utilized in biocontrol are *T. minutum*, *T. chilonis*,

T. evanescens, T. australicum, T. confusum, T. japonicum, T. brasilensis, T. armigera, T. orstrinae, T. acheae etc.

From order Diptera the family Tachinidae ranks first since it contain about 1500 parasitic species and play very important role in pest control (Askew, 1971).

Very thorough knowledge on biological relationships of this group is essential for correct manipulation of them in biopest control. Various relationships refers to solitary, gregarious, polyembryonic, monophagus, polyphagus, oligophagus, primary, secondary, tertiary, endo, exo, egg, egg-larval, larval, larval pupal, pupal, adult, auto and cleapto, hyper, super and multi parasitoid parasitism, etc. Certain behaviours of biocontrol agents have more importance since the success of the biocontrol is dependent on them. For instance, mating is essential for production of females and parthenogenetically only males are produced in parasitic hymenoptera. This adversely affect the biocontrol programme.

Biological control agents are assessed by taking into account of their life activities ex. longevity, life cycle, fecundity, searching ability of females for their hosts, host preferences, etc.

Parasitism behaviour is widely studied by several authors (Vinson, 1976; Cardona & Oatman 1971; Sathe 1991, 1993), since it is back bone of biological control. The behaviour typically consists a chain, host habitat selection – host selection – host suitability – host acceptance and oviposition. Various plant parts, allelochemicals play very important role in attracting the biocontrol agents towards their hosts via host habitat. Audio, visual and chemical ques are helpful in the process.

Predators

In the biological control the role of predators is also quite significant. The taxonomic and biological relationships of this group have been studied by Sweetman (1958) and Swan (1964). The predators are largely from Coleoptera. Neuroptera, Hemiptera, Diptera, Hymenoptera and Lepidoptera. The coccinelids alone contribute 4000 species. In the biocontrol history, cottony cushion scale was controlled with the help of a coccinelid beetle (Lady bird beetle) *Rodolia cardinalis* in 1988 in California. Since then, a very large number of predators have been utilized in the biocontrol programmes.

As like parasitoids, predators have also a very significant role in biological pest control. The predators are generally larger than their preys. They consume several preys (pests) in their life by hunting. Hence, they are more efficient than the parasitoids. The predators are widely scattered in several groups of animals like birds, reptiles, amphibians, mammals pisces, coelentrates, arachnids (spiders), insects, etc.

Class Insecta

The orders of class insecta like Coleoptera, Neuroptera, Hemiptera and Diptera provide a large number of predacious species. From Coleoptera, the family Coccinelidae alone gives 4000 predacious species and commonly called as Lady bird beetles (Coccinelid beetles). The coccinelid, *Menochilus sexmaculata* feed on many homopterous pests like aphids, mealy bugs, aleyrodids, etc. Likely *Coccinella* spp also feed on aphids. The tiger beetles, *Cicindela* spp feed on variety of small insects. The ground beetles, *Pheropsophus sorrinus* predates on the larvae of rhinocerous beetle, *Oryctes rhinococeros*. The hemipteran ruduviid, *Harpactor costalis* feed on red cotton bug, *Dysdercus* sp., Mirids, *Psollus* spp on thrips. While, the pentatomid bugs *Cantheconidia* sp. and *Andrallus* sp. feed on the larvae of *Heliothis armigera* and *Spodoptera litura*. The families Heliodinidae, Lycaenidae and Noctuidae of order lepidoptera also contain some predaceous species. The Heliodinid (*Stathmopoda* sp.) feed on some coccids.

As like Coleoptera, Neuroptera order has also great potential as predatory species and hence utilized prominantly in biocontrol of pest species. Lace wings and ant lions are prominant predators from this order. The praying mantids belongs to order Dictyoptera have also tremendous potential in suppression of pest populations. *Mantis religiosa* predates on several types of insect pests including Hemiptera and Lepidoptera, etc.

Invertebrate Predators

The spider, *Xystichus* spp. predate on several species of sawflies. Many species of mites are predaceous on insects belonging to more than 10 orders. The Coelentrates (hydra) *Chlorohydra* spp. are effective against mosquitoes, *Aedes higromaculis* while, Planaria, *Dugesia dorotocephala* is effective against *Culex* mosquitoes.

Vertebrate Predators

Many small species of pisces are insectivorous. They feed on larvae of mosquitoes and biting flies. The amphibians are practically mainly insectivorous. The toads *Bufo* spp. are very good biocontrol agents of insects. *Bufo marinus* was very successfully introduced in Puerto Rico in 1920 for controlling Junebeetles, mole crikets and cockroaches. The *gaint* toad feed on white grubs.

Birds

The birds have very significant role in biological pest control. Wood-peckers, wood warblers and certain migratory birds feed on bark beetles, spruce bud worms and pine saw flies respectively. The Indian mynah bird, *Acridotheres tristis* is classic example of biological control agent from birds. The Indian crows (gray striped) are found feeding very potentially on *Heliothis armigera* larvae.

Mammals

The bats (Chiroptera) feed on several nocturnal flying insect pests including locusts and certain moths. Moles and shrews are largely insectivorous. The Indian false vampire, *Megaderma lyra* feed on tasar silkmoths and grasshoppers. The stripped squirrel, *Funambulus pennanti* is effective biological control agent of crikets, *Gryllotalpa* sp., locusts and hoppers. Likely, foxes, jackals, wild dogs, domestic dogs, mongoose, cats, etc. are also good biological control agents of insects.

Pathogens

Since biological control has a broad base, pathogens are also widely used in the pest control programmes. 90 species of bacteria, 700 species of fungi, 210 species of protoza, 1000 species of nematodes, more than 3 species of rikettsiae and 450 species of viruses are visualized as biological control agents of a very large number of insect pests. The pathogens may exert their controlling effect by means of their invasive properties, by toxins, enzymes and other substrates.

Bacteria

Produce endo and exotoxins and cause mortalities in pest species. Endotoxins or toxic protein crystals paralyse the insect which results in cease feeding and the death. The exotoxins have high molecular weight and are adenine nucleotides which contain unusual sugar, allomuaic acid. It interfere with nucleic acid metabolism and protein synthesis and cause the mortality in target species.

Bacillus thuringiensis is very potent biocontrol agent of more than 150 caterpillars. Ex. Cabbage butterfly larvae, sugarcane borers, Tobaco caterpillar, *Plutella* sp., etc. *B. lentimorbus* and *B. fribourgensis* are effective against scarabid larvae. Biotrol, Dipel, Thuriciae, etc. are some important insecticides derived from bacterial spores/crystals by USDA.

Fungi

More than 700 species of fungi that normally invade through the host cuticle. The toxins produced by fungi cause death of large species. The spores germinate on cuticle, penetrate through chitin or respiratory organs or rarely via alimentary canal, reach to the tissues, hyphal bodies enter in haemocoel, results in death of insect. After the death hyphae comeout, spores formed, get dispersed by wind or rain or insects and again infest the insects.

Toxins produced by the species are identified in many species.

Species	Toxin	Pest
Entomopthora spp.	Protenaceous toxins	Aphids, Jassids, *Spilosoma obliqua*
Aspergillus flavus	Aflatoxin	Many insects
Beauveria bassiana	Beauvericin, Beauvero-lides, Bassinolides	Mealy bugs, cabbage lopper etc.
Metarrhizium anisopliae	Destruxin A,B,C,D,E,F	Spittle bug, mosquitoes, Rhinocerous beetle, Field criket, etc.

Beauvericin induce cellular alterations, especially at the nuclear level. Destruxins and other toxins seem to be involved in the pathogenic process by blocking the cellular immunoreactions.

Administration of mycotoxins renders the host more sensitive to infection.

There is need to identify fungal toxins to enable their commercial development for insects control. At present there are no fungal metabolites under commercial development as insecticides. However, certain mycoinsecticides are under development in various countries like USSR, USA, UK, China, France, Brazil, Australia, etc.

Viruses

Viron particles enter through mouth or digestive tract, infect or pass through gut epithelium then enter in susceptible host tissue, multiply in host body, and results sudden and dramatic outburst and Death.

Symptoms : Slugishness, skin become fragile, reputurned easily.

Types of Viruses : NPV, CPV, NIV, GV etc.

Insects controlled : Cutworm *Spodoptera litura* (NPV), Saw flies (NPV), *P. rapae, P. brassicae* (GV), *Heliothis armigera, H. zea, H. virescens* (NPV), spruce bud worm (NPV, CPV, GV), *Cydia pomonella* (GV), Gypsy moth, *Lymentria disper* (NPV) etc. Many species are under trial.

Rikettsiae

Rikettsiae are placed between viruses and bacteria and have callular structure containing DNA & RNA and are bound by a cell wall containing muramic acid.

Important spp. and their hosts

Enterella stethorae – Beetle, *Stethorus* sp.

Rickettsiella popillae – *Popillia japonica*

R. melolonthae – *Melolontha melolontha*

R. tipulae – *Tipula paludose*

R. chironomi – *chironomids*

Research work on insect specific species is needed.

Protozoa

Large number of protozoans are parasitic on insects. They cause chronic diseases and take more time to kill hosts. Protozoans reduce efficiency of reproduction and physiological functions. *Microsporidia* affects at least 14 orders of insects but, more commonly Diptera & Lepidoptera. About 150 microsporidians are entomogenus. Hosts : P. *brassicae*, C. *pomonella*, H. *zea*, O. *nubilalis*, etc. *Glugea* sp. attack O. *nubilalis* and C. *fumiferana*.

Nematodes

More than 1000 species are known as entomogenous. The families Mermithidae, Neoaplectaonidae and Allantonematidae are most important. Some more important genera includes *Mermis*, *Geomermis*, *Hexamermis*, etc. Hosts : A. *moorei*, grasshoppers, caddis flies, *Chilotrea infuscatellus* etc.

Recent Advances in Biological Control

1. The use of neuropeptides.

2. Protoplast fusion between an insecticidal B.t. var. *kurstaki* HD 73 and plant growth promoting *Rhizobacterial* strain of *Pseudomonas fluorescens* PFCP.

3. *Tissue culture* : The importance of insect tissue culture for possible mass multiplication and utilization of polydna viruses of certain females of Ichneumonid and Braconid parasitic insects to overcome the abgation of their defence mechanism and there by increasing efficiency of biological control of certain crop pests should be highlighted.

4. *Genetic engineering* : The recombinant NPVS can function as growth regulators and viral pesticides with increased insecticidal activity carrying toxin/neuropeptide genus of heterologus origin.

5. *Specific pesticides* : Safer for natural enemies should be investigated.

6. *Synthetic diet for Biocontrol agents* : ex. *Trichogramma* spp., coccinelids, etc.

7. Possible research activities related to hybridization of monophagus and polyphagus parasitoids.

CHAPTER 6

SUMMARY

The protection of agricultural crops from various kinds of pests is a chronic problem. Several insect orders cause the damage to agricultural crops by defoliating, leaf mining, sucking the cell sap, boring various parts, forming galls, etc. The introduction of high yielding varieties have also increased the pest problems. During last 50 years, the use of chemical insecticides has been increased enormously resulting many serious problems like ari & water pollution, health hazards, killing of beneficial organisms, destruction of natural balance and ecological cycle, pest resistance, pest resurgence and secondary pest out-break, etc. This clearly indicates that there is an urgent need of alternative for chemical insecticides. In this context, biological pest control is "living weapon" over chemical control.

The baraconids (Hymenoptera : Braconidae) are potential biocontrol agents of insect pests. They parasitize the pests and cause mortalities in them. Hence, they are widely used in biological pest control programmes in the world (Rao *et al.* 1971; Coopel & Mertins, 1977). The braconids are reported on several major orders of the insect pest like Lepidoptera Coleoptera, Hemiptera and rarely Hymenoptera. More than 40,000 species of braconids have been reported from the world (Achterberg, 1987). However, economic exploitation of the braconids will be possible and fruitful if we have information on their taxonomy, distributional records and host records. Keeping in view the above facts, present topic was selected.

The present study will be helpful for exploiting the braconid parasitoids in biocontrol programmes of pests, ecological studies and making host parasitoid index of the region.

BIBLIOGRAPHY

vanAchterberg, C. 1988. Parellelisms in the braconidae (Hymenoptera) with special reference to biology. *Advances in Parasitic Hymenoptera Research*, pp. 85-115.

vanAchterberg, C. and Narendran, T.C. 1997. Notes on the types and type depositories of Braconidae (Insecta : Hymenoptera) described by T.C. Narendran and students. *Zool. Med. Leiden*, **71**, 177-179.

Ashmead, W.H. 1898, Description of new parasitic Hymenotera. *Proc. ent. Soc. Wash.*, **4**, 155-171.

Ashmead, W.H. 1904. A List of the Hymenoptera of the Philippine Island. *J.N.Y. ent. Soc.*, **12**, 1-22.

Ashmead, W.H. 1905. New Hymmenoptera from the Philippine Island. *Proc. U.S. nat. Mus.*, **29**, 107-199.

Ayyar, T.V.R. 1920. On the insect parasites of some Indian crop pests. *Proc. Ent. Mtgs. Pusa*, **3**, 931-936.

Ayyar, T.V.R. 1921. A list of parasitic Hymenoptera of economic importance from South India. *Proc. Ent. Mtgs. Pusa*, 4, 363-366.

Ayyar, T.V.R. 1926. On the Braconid genus *Aphrasloracon* (parasite on Eublemma). *Bull. Ent. Res*, **17**, 91-98.

Ayyar, T.V.R. 1928. A contribution to our knowledge of the South Indian Braconidae. *Mem. Dep. Agric. India*, **10**, 29-60.

Besson, C.F.C. and Chatterjee, S.N., 1935. On the biology of Braconidae (Hymenoptera). *Indian Forest Rec.* (N.S.) *Ent.*, **1**, 105-138.

Bhat, Shama and Gupta, V.K. 1977. Ichneumonologia orientalis Part VI, The subfamily Agathidinae (Hymenoptera: Braconidae). *Oriental ins.* (monograph), **6**, 1-345.

Bhatnagar, S.P. 1948. Studies on *Apanteles* Foerster (Vipionidae : Parasitic hymenoptera) from India. *Indian J. Ent.*, **10**, 133-203.

Bingham, C.T. 1901. Description of two new species of *Bracon* from Bengal. *Ann. Mag. Nat. Hist.*, **8**, 555-557.

Brulle, A. 1846. In Lepeletier : *Histoire Naturelle des Insectes, Hymenoptera*, **4**, 689.

Cameron, P. 1891. Hymenopterological notices. *Mem. Proc. Manchester Lit. Phil. Soc.*, **4**, 185-194.

Cameron, P. 1900. Hymenoptera orientalia, or contributions to the knowledge of the Hymenoptera of the oriental zoological region. Part 9. The Hymenoptera of the Khasia Hills. Part 11. Section 1. *Mem. Proc. Manchester Lit. Phil. Soc. 44*, pp. 114.

Cameron, P. 1905. A third contribution to the knowledge of the Hymenoptera of Sarawak. *J. Straits. Branch. Royal Asiatic Soc.*, **44**, 93-168.

Cameron, P. 1906. On the hymenopterous parasites of the mealie stalk borer (*Sesamia fusca* Hamps). *Trans S. Afr. Soc.*, **17**, 334-336.

Cameron, P. 1907. On the Prasitic Hymenoptera collected by Major C.G. Nurse in the Bombay Presidency. *J. Bombay Nat. Hist. Soc.*, **17**, 578-597.

Cameron, P. 1910 a. On some Asiatic species of the subfamilies Braconinae and Exothecinae in the Royal Berlin Museum. *Societies Entomologia*, **25**, 19-20.

Cameron, P. 1910 b. On some Asiatic species of the subfamilies Braconinae and Exothecinae in the Royal Berlin Museum. *Societies Entomologia*, **25**, 22-23.

Cameron, P. 1910 c. On some Asiatic species of the subfamilies Exothecinae, Spathinae, Hormioinae, Cheloninae and Macrocentrinae in the Royal Berlin Zoological Museum. *Tidschriff voor Entomologia*, **53**, 41-55.

Cameron, P. 1911. On a collection of parasitic Hymenoptera (Chiefly bred) made by Mr. W.W. Froggatt in New South Wales, with descriptions of new genera and species. *Proc. Linn. Soc. N.S.W;* **36**, 342.

Cameron, P. 1912. On a collection of parasitic hymenoptera (Chiefly bred), made by Mr. W.W. Froggatt, in New South Wales, with descriptions of new genera and species. *Proc. Linn. Soc. N.S.W; 37,* 172-216.

Cameron, P. 1913. On the parasitic Hymenoptera reared at Dehra Dun, Northern India, from the lac (Tachardia) and Sal Insects. *Indian Forest Rec., 4,* 91-100.

Chalikwar, M.R. 1974. Studies on parasitic hymenoptera of Marathwada with special reference to family Braconidae, Ph. D. thesis, pp. 1-260.

Chalikwar, M.R.; Rao, S.N. and Nikam, P.K. 1982. Two new species of *Cotesia* Cameron (Hymenoptera:Bracondiae). *Oriental Ins., 18,* 17-23.

Chatterjee, P.N. 1941. Notes on the some parasites on Shisham defoliators at Allahabad and Dehra Dun, India. *Indian. J. Ent., 3,* 157-172.

Dawale, R.K. 1991. Studies on the natural enemies of some economic important crop pests with special reference of Hymenoptera. Ph.D. thesis, Shivaji University, Kolhapur, pp. 1-213.

Dawale, R.K. Bhosale, Y.A. and Sathe, T.V. 1992. A new species of genus *Charops* Holmgren (Hymenoptera : Ichneumonidae) from India. *Asian J. Zool. Sci., 1,* 19-23.

Dawale, R.K. Bhosale, Y.A. and Sathe, T.V. 1993. A new species of genus *Cotesia* Cameron. (Hymenoptera : Braconidae) from India. *Bioved, 4,* 263-266.

Foerster, A. 1862. *Verh. natur. Ver. Preuss. Rhind'un, 19,* 245.

Gupta, V.K. 1957. Some species of *Apanteles* Foerster and their hyperparasites from India with descriptions of new species (Parasitic Hymenoptera). *Indian J. Ent., 19,* 101-106.

Gupta, V.K. 1987. Advances in parasitic Hymenoptera research, pp. 1-7.

Halidy, A.H. 1833. Essay on the classification of parasitic Hymenoptera. *Ent. Mag., 1,* 480-491.

Inamdar, S.A. 1990. Biosystematic studies of braconid parasitoids of some economic important crop pests in Western Maharashtra. Ph.D. thesis, Shivaji University, Kolhapur, pp. 1-216.

Ingawale, D.M. 1991. Biosystematic studies on Microgastrinae of some important economic crop pest. Ph. D. thesis, Shivaji University, Kolhapur, pp., 1-200.

Ingawale, D.M. and Sathe, T.V. 1993. On a new species of the genus *Rhygoplitis* Gahan (Hymenoptera : Braconidae) from India. *Oikossay,* 10, 39-40.

Kerrich, G.J. 1960. The state of our knowledge of the systematics of the Hymenoptera Parasitica. *Trans. Soc. Brit. Entomol.,* 14, 1-18.

Lal, K.B. 1939. Some new species of Hymenoptera from India. *Indian J. Ent.* 1, 49-58.

Lal, K.B. 1942. Description of two new and redescription of third species of *Apanteles* (Braconidae) from India. *Indian J. Ent.,* 4, 163-166.

Mason, W.R. M. 1981. The polyphyletic nature of *Apanteles* Foerster (Hymenoptera : Braconidae), a phylogeny and reclassification of microgastrinae. *Ent. Soc. Canada,* 115, 1-147.

Mathur, R.N. 1942. On the biology of the parasites of the shisham defoliators in the Punjab Plantations. *Indian Forest Rec. (N.S.) Ent.* 7, 9-65.

Narayanan, E.S. 1936. Importance of the study of hymenopterous parasites in India with notes of the bionomics of some of the important parasites found in Pusa. *Proc. Ind. Sci. Cong.,* Indore, 23, pp. 453.

Narayanan, E.S. and Subbarao, B.R. 1960. New species of Encyrtid and Braconid parasites. *Indian J. Ent.,* 22, 75-79.

Narendran, T.C., P.K. Sumodan and Rema, C.G. 1992. A study of Indian species of *Chelonus* Panzer (Hymenoptera : Braconidae). *J. Zool. Soc. Kerala,* 2, 1-9.

Narendran, T.C., C.G. Rema and Madhavikatty, M. 1994. Three new species of *Cassidibracon* Quicke (Hymenoptera : Bracondiae) from India. *Bioved,* 5, 125-132.

Narendran, T.C. and Rema, C.G. 1996. Three species of Braconidae (Hymenoptera) from India. *Indian J. Ecobiol.,* **8,** 135-142.

Nixon, G.E.J. 1965. A reclassification of the tribe Micorgastrini (Hymenoptera : Braconidae). *Bull. Br. Mus. Nat. Hist., (ent).,* **2,** 1-284.

Nixon, G.E.J. 1967. The Indo-Australian species of the Ultor group of *Apanteles* Foerster (Hymenoptera : Braconidae). *Bull. Br. Mus. Nat. Hist. (ent).,* **21,** 1-34.

Papp, J. 1986. A Survey of the European species of *Apanteles* Forst. ‏(Hymenoptera, Braconidae : Microgastrinae) IX. The *glomeratus* group, 1. *Annls. hist. nat. Mus. natn. hung,* **78,** 225-247.

Papp, J. 1987. A survey of the European species of *Apanteles* Forst. (Hymenoptera, Braconidae : Mocrogastrinae), X. The *glomeratus*-group. 2 and the *cultellatus* group. *Annls. hist. nat. Mus. natu. hund.,* **79,** 207-258.

Rao, S.N. 1953. Notes on some parasitic hymenoptera from India with the description of a new speceis, *Apanteles epijarbi. Indian. J. Ent.,* **15,** 23-28.

Rao, S.N. 1961. Key to the Oriental species of *Apanteles* Foerster (Hymenoptera). *Proc. Nat. Acad. Sci. India. B,* **31,** 32-46.

Rao, S.N. and Chalikwar, M.R. 1970 a. A new species of the genus *Apanteles* Foerster (Hymenoptera : Braconidae) from Marathwada. *Bull. Ent.,* **11,** 11-14.

Rao, S.N. and Chalikwar, M.R. 1970 b. Studies on Indian parasitic Hymenoptera (Braconidae) from Marathwada, I. *Marathwada Uni. J. Sci.,* **9,** 107-112.

Rao, S.N. and Chalikwar, M.R. 1970 c. Four new species of the Braconid genus *Protomicroplitis* Ashmead from India and a key to the oriental species. *Bull. Ent.,* **11,** 102-115.

Rao, S.N. and Chalikwar, M.R. 1971. Studies on parasitic hymenoptera (Braconidae) from Marathwada, III. Three new species of *Chelonus* Panzer. *Oriental. Ins.,* **5,** 469-476.

Rao, S.N. and Kurian, C. 1950. Description of eleven new and records of fifteen known species of Ichneumonidae (Hymenoptera parasitica from India Part I). *Indian. J. Ent.,* **12,** 167-190.

Rema, C.G., and Narendran, T.C. 1996. A remarkable new genus of Braconidae (Hymenoptera) from India. *J. Bombay nat. Hist. Soc.*, **93**, 264-267.

Rokade, A.G. 1996. "Studies on Braconid Parasitoids from Maharashtra". M.Phil. thesis, Shivaji University, Kolhapur pp. 1-91.

Sathe, T.V. 1992. A new species of the genus *Rhygoplitis* Gahan (Hymenoptera : Braconidae) in India. *J. Zool. Res;* **5**, 13-16.

Sathe, T.V. and Inamdar, S.A. 1988. A new species of the genus *Nyereria* Wilkinson (Hymenoptera : Braconidae) from India. *J. Adv. Zool.*, **9**, 128-131.

Sathe, T.V. and Inamdar, S.A. 1989 a. A new species of the genus *Apanteles* Foerster (Hymenoptera : Braconidae) from Western Maharashtra. *Oikoassay,* **6**, 5-7.

Sathe, T.V. and Inamdar, S.A. 1989 b. A new species of the genus *Hypomicrogaster* Ashmead (Hymenoptera : Braconidae) from India. *Indian J. Inv. Zool & Aqua. Biol.*, **1**, 21-23.

Sathe, T.V. and Inamdar, S.A. 1991. Two new species of the genus *Glylptapanteles* Ashmead and *Parenion* Nixon (Hymenoptera : Braconidae) from India. *Hexapoda*, **3**, 89-83.

Sathe, T.V. and Ingawale, D.M. 1995. Two new species of the genus *Apanteles* Foerster (Hymenoptera : Braconidae) from India. *J. Bombay Nat. Hist. Soc.*, **92**, 81-84.

Sathe, T.V., R.K. Dawale and Ingawale D.M. 1989. A new species of the genus *Parapanteles* Ashmead (Hymenoptera : Braconidae) from India. *Indian J. Parasitol;* **13**, 211-213.

Sathe, T.V., D.M. Ingawale and Bhosale Y.A. 1994. Two new species of the genus *Cotesia* Cameron (Hymenoptera : Braconidae) from India. *Hexapoda*, **6**, 79-85.

Smith, F. (1860). Catalogue of hymenopterous insects collected by Mr. A.R. Wallace in the Islands of Bachian, Kaisaa, Amboyna, Gilolo and at Dory in New Guainea. *Proc. Linnean Soc.* (Zool); **5**, 93-143.

Sumodan, P.K. and Narendran, T.C. 1990. Five new species of *Apanteles* Foerster (Hymenoptera : Braconidae) from Kerala, India. *J. Ecobiol.*, **2**, 239-248.

Telanga, N.A. 1955. Preponchatokrylye Sem. Braconidae, podesem. *Microgastrinae*, Dodsem. Agathinae (Hymenoptera : family Braconidae, subfamily Microgastrinae, subfamily Agathinae). *Fauna USSR*, **5**, 1-312.

Tobias, V.I. 1976. Novye vidy Naexdnikav-Braconid iz Roda *Apanteles* Frost. (Hymeoptera : Braconidae). *S. Dalnego Votoka Trudy Zool. Inst.*, **67**, 90-96.

Viereck, H.L. 1909. Hymenoptera for the New Jersey, list of insects and other Hymenoptera. *Proc. ent. Soc.* Washington D.C., **11**, 208-211.

Viereck, H.L. 1911. Description of six new genera and thirty one new species of Ichneumon flies. *Proc. U.S. nat. Mus.* **40**, 170-196.

Watanabe, C. 1934. On some species of Braconidae from Formosa and Phillippines in the Deutsches Entomologisehes Museum. *Ins. Matsumurana*, **8**, 119-123.

Watanabe, C. 1935. H. Sauter's Formosa Collection, Braconidae. *Ins. Matsumurana*, **8**, 182-205.

Watanabe, C. 1936. On two hymenopterous guests of ants in Japan. *Ins. Matsumurana*, **9**, 90-94.

Watanabe, C. 1937. A contribution to the Braconid fauna of the Empire of Japan. *J. Fac. Agri. Hokkaido Univ.*, **42**, 1-188.

Wilkinson, D.S. 1927. On the Indo-Malayan species of the genus *Microgaster* (Hymenoptera : Braconidae). *Bull. ent. Res.*, **18**, 171-178.

Wilkinson, D.S. 1928 a. A revision of the Indo-Australlian species of the genus *Apanteles* (Hymenoptera : Braconidae) Part I. *Bull. ent. Res.*, **19**, 79-105.

Wilkinson, D.S. 1928 b. A revision of the Indo-Australlian species of the genus *Apanteles* (Hymenoptera : Braconidae) Part II. *Bull. Ent. Res.*, **19**, 109-146.

Wilkinson, D.S. 1929. New parasitic Hymenoptera and notes on other species. *Bull. ent. Res.*, **20**, 103-144.

Wilkinson. D.S. 1930. New Braconidae and other notes. *Bull. ent. Res.*, **21**, 275-285.

Wilkinson, D.S. 1932 a. Four new *Apanteles*. *Stylops*, 1, 139-144.

Wilkinson, D.S. 1932 b. A revision of the Ethiopian species of the genus *Apanteles* (Hymenoptera : Braconidae). *Trans, R. ent. Soc. Lond.*, 80, 301-344.

Wilkinson, D.S. 1935. Two new *Apanteles* (Hymenoptera : Braconidae). *Stylops*, 4, 266-269.

SUBJECT INDEX

A

Advantages 101
Apantelini 4
Applications 96
Application does 100

B

Bacteria 106
Biocontrol agents 98
Biological control 95
Braconids 2

C

Cotesiini 5
Crop 99

D

Diptera 99
Disadvantages 101

E

Early history 95
Ecological basis 95

F

Future of biocontrol 97
Fungi 106

G

Genetic engineering 108

H

Host record 7
Hybridization 108
Hymenoptera 1

M

Methods 97
Microgastrinae 3
Monophagus 108

N

Natural enemies 99, 100
Nematodes 107
Neuropeptides 107

P

Parasitoids 98, 102
Pathogen 105
Pest 96, 100, 106
Phylogeny 62
Polyphagus 108
Predators 99, 103
Protoplast fusion 108
Protozoa 108

R

Rikettisae 107

S

Specific pesticides 108
Survey 6
Synthetic diet 108

T

Taxonomy 1, 14
Tissue culture 108
Toxins 106

V

Viruses 107

SPECIES INDEX

A

Achea janata 39, 99
A. moorei 107
Acridotheres tristis 95
Adelius 3
Alhomelou 4
Apanteles spp. 98
   arachi 21
   antipoda 20
   banksi 61, 62
   belippae 45
   brachmiae 40
   cague 50
   cajae 55
   callimone 60
   chilocida 35, 50, 55
   cirphicola 55
   congregatus 15
   erionotae 24, 30
   errator 30
   euchaeties 35
   eulhallae 20
   fakhralhajiae 82
   hemithae 67, 72
   hyblaeae 82
   lipsis 67
   longitangiae 72
   objectus 40
   obliguae 88
   oidemataphori 77
   pachkariae 82
   papillionis 45
   pieridis 20
   ricinii 67
   ruficrus 45, 50, 60
   ruidus 24
   salebrosus 24
   saltator 45
   sesamae 15, 88
   taenioticornis 77
   taprobannae 40, 60
   valvulae 27
Aphelinus mali 99
Aphytis melinus
Archis hypogae 23
Aspergillus flavus 106

B

Bacillus fribourgensis 106
   lentimorbus 106
   thuringinensis 106
Beauveria bassiana 106
Bracon brevicornis 96
Bracon krikpatrikii 101
Buluca 5

C

Cajanus cajan 59
Chilo spp. 96
Chilonus blakburni 101
Chilo partellus 93, 98
   sacchariphaga indicus 101
   suppressalis 34
Chilotraea infuscatellus 108
Choeras 5
Chrysopa spp. 100
Clarkinella 5

Cotesia anari 16, 17
  arachi 21, 25
  bazari 26, 27
  chiloi 31, 33
  flavipes 15, 30, 35
  fumiferana 108
  glomeratus 2
  janati 36, 37
  mangiferi 41, 43
  paranari 46, 49
  sunfloweri 51, 54
  tuski 56, 58
Cryptochaetam 95
Cryptolaemus spp. 96
Cryptolaemus montrouzieri 100
Crysoperla carnea 100
Cydia pomonella 107, 108

D

Dasylagan 4
Dirrhope 3
Dolichogenidea 4, 5
  exiguvi 63, 66
  lycoperci 68, 70
  mythimna 73, 75
  sunflowari 78, 81, 82

E

Encarsia spp. 99
Enterella stethorae 107
Entomopthora spp. 106
Erias 96
Eriosoma lanigerum 99
Euproctis lunata 59
Eurogaster ecdytolophae 89
Exorista bombycis 100
Exoryza 4
Exulonyx 4

G

Geomermis 108
Glugea spp. 108

Glyptapanteles 5, 83
  malshri 88
  mamlae 83
  melanitis 84, 87
Gonizous nephantidis 96

H

Helianthus annus 53, 80
Heliothis 96
Heliothis armigera 99, 100, 107
H. virescens 107
H. zea 107, 108
Hypomicrogaster 4, 89
  ecus 89
  moscus 89
  mineri 22, 90
  suffolciensis 89
  solox 89
  tiro 89
  tydeus 89

I

Icerya purchesi 95, 99
Iconella 5
Illidops 4
Inderbella tetraonis 44
Isotima javensis 98

L

Laptomastix spp. 96
Latoia lepida 29
Lycopersicum escalentum 71
Lymentria disper 107

M

Maconellicocous hirsutus 101
Mangifera indica 44
Melanitis ismene 86
Melanospis glomerata 99
Melolontha melolontha 107
Mermis 107
Meteorus dichomeridis 101

Microgaster 3, 89
  diaphamiae 89
  ecdytolophae 89
  jacarae 89
  zonaria 89, 94
Microplitis 3
Micropotes 4
Mythimna separata 76

N

Nephantis serinopa 99
Nesolynx thymus 101
Nomadocris septemfaciata 95

O

Oryza sativa 34, 36
Opius spp. 99
O. nubilalis 107

P

Papillia japonica 107
Parnara mathias 48
Pectinophora 96
P. gossypiella 99
P. brassicae 107, 108
P. rapae 107
Pennisetam typhoides 29
Pisum sativam 65
Plutella spp. 106

R

Rhizobacteria 108
R. chironomi 107
R. melolonthae 107
R. tipulae 107
Ricinus communis 39
Rickettsiella popillae 107

Rodalia cardinalis 95, 99, 103

S

Scymnus spp. 6
Sorghum vulgarae 76
Spodoptera exiguva 65
Spodoptera litura 65, 107
Spoggosia beniziana 99
Spilosoma obliqua 53, 81, 101,
  106
Sticholotis medayssae 99

T

Telanomus spp. 99
Tipula paludose 107
Trichogramma spp. 96, 98, 101
  acheae 98, 103
  armigera 98, 103
  australicum 98, 103
  brasilensis 98, 99, 103
  chilonis 98, 102
  confusum 98, 103
  evanescens 98, 103
  japonicum 98, 103
  minutum 98, 102
  orstrinae 98, 103
Tryporyza nivella 98

V

Virachola isocrates 19

X

Xanthopimpla punctata 98

Z

Zea mays 48, 93